PEARSON   ALWAYS LEARNING

Kathleen M. McLaughlin • Dorothy B. Wakefield

An Introduction to DATA ANALYSIS Using MINITAB® 17

Fifth Edition for University of Connecticut

Taken from:
An Introduction to DATA ANALYSIS
Using MINITAB for Windows, Third Edition
by Kathleen M. McLaughlin and Dorothy B. Wakefield

Cover Art: Courtesy of Pearson Learning Solutions.

Taken from:

An Introduction to DATA ANALYSIS Using MINITAB for Windows, Third Edition
by Kathleen M. McLaughlin and Dorothy B. Wakefield
Copyright © 2005 by Pearson Education, Inc.
Upper Saddle River, New Jersey 07458

This special edition published in cooperation with Pearson Learning Solutions.

Pearson Learning Solutions, 501 Boylston Street, Suite 900, Boston, MA 02116
A Pearson Education Company
www.pearsoned.com

Printed in the United States of America

19   17

000200010271938799

SV

ISBN 10: 1-323-01363-6
ISBN 13: 978-1-323-01363-2

This book is dedicated to our families:
Fred, Madison, Anna, Hayley, Ryan, Hannah, Jack, Rob, Dan,
and Chrissy who are "significantly" wonderful. (P=.00000)

Introduction

This MINITAB lab manual is designed to be used with any Elementary Statistics textbook. The lessons are self-explanatory and explore topics that are covered in all elementary texts.

Each chapter has an instructional section which summarizes a basic statistical concept. This is followed by a computer assignment in which students can practice the techniques that they have learned in the chapter.

All the data sets used in the lessons are saved on a data CD as MINITAB Worksheets (*.MTW).

All instructions and diagrams in the manual were developed using MINITAB Release 17. The data sets were also created in MINITAB 17.

Our purpose in writing this manual is to provide some simple and practical examples of basic statistical techniques so that students can see that statistics is more than just a long list of mind-boggling formulas. Since MINITAB does all the computation, students can concentrate on selecting the appropriate statistical method and can focus on understanding and interpreting the results.

Note to Instructors:

All MINITAB worksheets used in the Assignment sections have multiple versions numbered from 1 to 4. For example, in Problem 1 of Assignment 1 the file ETHNIC1.MTW is used. ETHNIC2.MTW through ETHNIC4.MTW also exist on the Data CD. Our intention was to provide different data so that an instructor can vary the assignments from semester to semester.

Table of Contents

Chapter I

Qualitative Data Analysis

Qualitative data is another name for categorical data. That is, the data is count data indicating the number of observations that fall into each category. For example, the chairperson of the Math Department might be interested in the number of males and females taking a Calculus course. In this example, the categories are Male and Female, and we would simply count how many students are in each category.

Once the data has been collected, it is necessary to summarize the data so that it is easier to understand the overall pattern. The data can be presented in a frequency table, but more often it is displayed graphically using either a bar chart or a pie chart. In general, a graphical display is both simple to make and easy to understand. The goal is to give the reader a quick overview of the data. Many newspapers and magazines use these graphs to get a reader's attention. We will be learning how to create bar charts and pie charts using MINITAB.

Bar Charts:

Bar charts are very simple to create using MINITAB. One thing to keep in mind is that any chart is incomplete without proper labeling. A title should describe the data in a short phrase. The graph should also have labels on both the x-axis and the y-axis. Normally the x-axis will have the different categories, so the axis label should describe the categories. The y-axis will have the counts or frequency for each category, so the axis label may be as simple as 'frequency' or 'count'.

For this practice example we will open a MINITAB worksheet named **Grad Degrees.MTW** which contains data that shows the number of students by School/College who graduated at the University in 2012.

To do this, click on: FILE → OPEN WORKSHEET.

On the screen that appears, you must tell MINITAB where the worksheet data is located. All the data is located in the Data Files Minitab 17 folder. (Fig. 1-1)

• •

Fig. I-I

To open the worksheet **GradDegrees**, scroll through the list of MTW (Minitab Worksheet files) and click on **GradDegrees** and then click on **Open**. (Fig. 1-2)

• •

Fig. I-2

The spreadsheet in the Data Window should now contain the data that we want to use. Notice that the data is for two different degrees: Master's and Doctorate. To begin, we will use only the data from Master's Degrees to create a bar chart. Column 3 (C3), called NUMBER, contains the number of students in each school who earned Master's degrees in 2012. Column2 (C2), called SCHOOL, contains the categories. In this case, the categories are the names of the different schools within the university. The DEGREE is the Master's Degree (C1).

To create the bar chart, click on: GRAPH → BAR CHART

The following pop-up screen will appear. Click on the down arrow beside the field **Bars represent** and select **Values from a table.** Highlight a **Simple** bar chart and click **OK**. (Fig. 1-3)

•••••••••••••••••••••••
Fig. I-3

The main bar chart input screen (Fig. 1-4) has many options that you can select. You can select the options before drawing the chart, or once the chart is drawn, you can edit the chart to make any desired changes.

• •

Fig. I-4

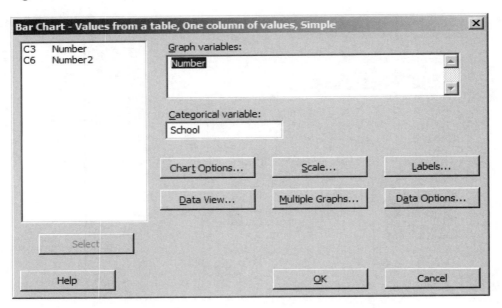

To create the Bar Chart you must select an entry for the **Graph variables** and for the **Categorical variable**. Minitab is expecting a numeric variable for the **Graph variables** and will only display the columns that contain numeric variables in the box to the left of the screen. Select C3 Number by double-clicking on it in the box at the left. Tab down to the field labeled **Categorical variable.** A list of categorical variables should appear in the box at the left. Double-click on C2 School to select it. If you click on **OK** now, a bar chart using all of Minitab's default values should appear on your screen. (Fig. 1-5)

. . . .

Fig. I-5

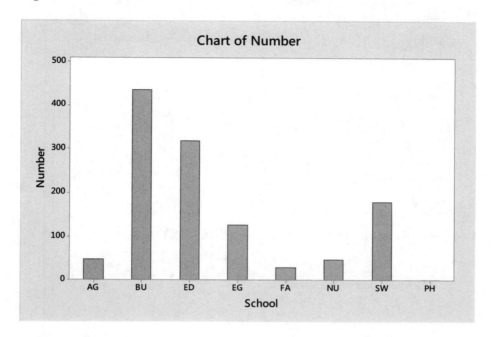

Before printing this chart, there are a few changes that will improve the appearance and readability of the chart. You could close this graph and go back to the GRAPH menu and enter a title, however, it is very easy to edit the chart itself. Double-click on the title of the graph. The following screen will pop up. (Fig. 1-6)

· · · · · · · · · · · · · · · · · · · ·

Fig. I-6

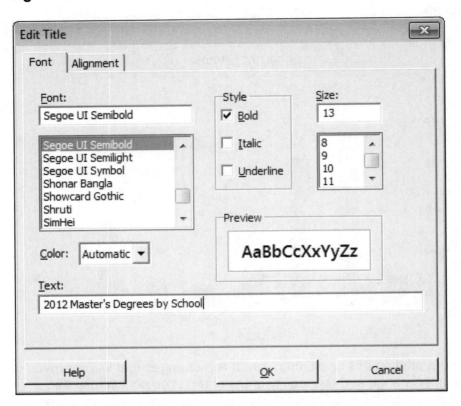

Below **Text** (at the bottom), replace the current title (Fig.1-6) by entering: 2012 Master's Degrees by School. Click on **OK**. The title should automatically be changed on the bar chart. You should make one other change to this chart. The y-axis label is "Number". It would be more descriptive if the label was "Number of Students". Double-click on the word "Number" on the chart. Below **Text** (at the bottom), replace the current axis title by entering: Number of Students. Click on **OK** for the final bar chart. (Fig. 1-7)

• •

Fig. I-7

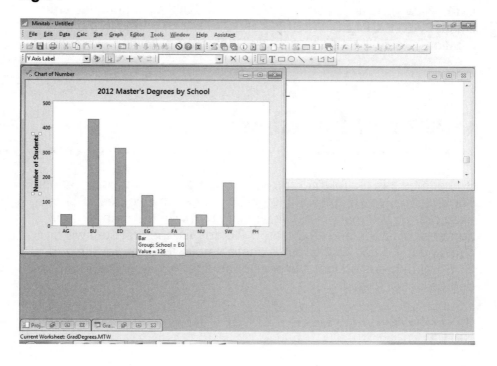

If you use your cursor and roll over a particular bar, Minitab will display more information on that particular bar. For example, we see that in the school of Engineering, 126 Master's Degrees were awarded in 2012.

If the bar chart looks good, then you are ready to print it. You have a few options for printing the graph. While the chart is still on your screen, click on: **FILE → PRINT GRAPH.** This will print the Graph Window for you. Another option is to open a Word document and then click on **EDIT → COPY GRAPH** and then paste the graph into your Word document. You can close the Graph Window by clicking on the **"X"** in the upper right corner of the Graph Window. This will bring you back to the Data and Session Windows. Note: These instructions explain how to print a graph but it is not necessary to actually print this example.

Cut and Paste:
• •

At times, it is necessary to either combine data or separate a small subset of the data. MINITAB uses the CUT & PASTE method that is used in many Windows applications. To use the CUT & PASTE method, highlight the entire section of the data that you wish to copy, click on **EDIT** on the top menu, and from the pull-down menu, click on **COPY CELLS**. Next, click on the cell where you want to "paste" the data. Now you can "paste" by clicking on **EDIT** again, but this time select **PASTE CELLS**. The data should now be added to the new location. You will be using "cut & paste" in the following example.

Clustered Bar Charts:

Sometimes it is useful to group data together by a particular variable. For instance, you might want to group the data by Degree. For this example, we will make a clustered bar chart with the data for both degrees (Master's and Doctorate). To do this, the first step will be to combine the data. Using "cut & paste", move the data for the Doctoral degrees so that it is positioned directly below the Master's degree data. (Fig. 1-8)

Fig. I-8

MINITAB can easily do a clustered bar chart for this combined data. From the bar chart pop-up screen (GRAPH → BAR CHART), select **Values from a table** and **Cluster.** (Fig. 1-9) Click on **OK**.

Chapter I: Qualitative Data Analysis

Fig. I-9

The following input screen will appear. It looks very much like the input screen used for a simple bar chart. (Fig. 1-10)

● ●

Fig. I-10

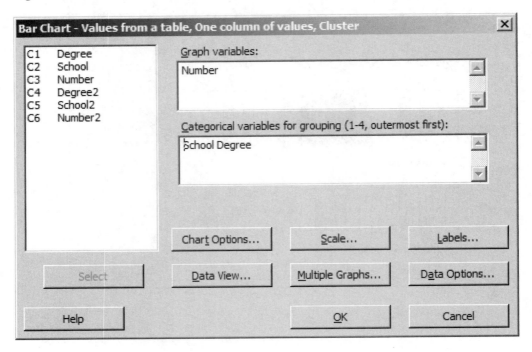

Notice that on this screen, you can enter more than one **Categorical variable**. Select C3 Number for the **Graph variable** by double-clicking on it in the box at the left. Tab down to the field labeled **Categorical variables for grouping.** A list of categorical variables should appear in the box at the left. Double-click on C2 School to select it as the outermost variable, and then double-click on C1 Degree. The outermost variable, C2 School, is the cluster variable. The bar chart will display the data clustered by School.   (Fig. 1-10) Click on **OK** to view the clustered bar chart. (Fig. 1-11) Change the titles on the clustered chart to titles of your choice.

· ·
Fig. I-II

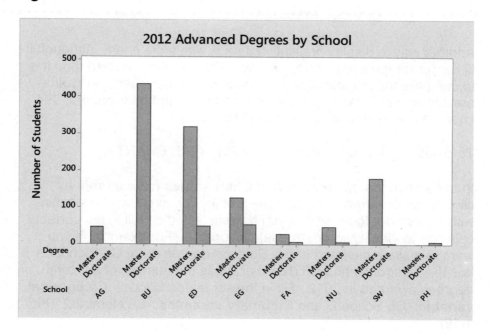

Because it is grouped, you can now see the advanced degrees in each School within the university. Comparisons are much easier to make using a clustered bar chart rather than using separate charts for each degree. Now print the graph or copy it into your Word document, close the Graph Window and return to the Data and Session Windows.

Pie Charts:

Another way to display qualitative data is with a pie chart. Although it is harder for the eye to compare two "slices" of the pie chart than it is to compare the heights of two rectangles on a bar chart, pie charts are still very popular, especially in magazines and newspapers. Pie charts are very simple to make in MINITAB.

To create a pie chart, click on: GRAPH → PIE CHART

In the screen that appears, select **Chart values from a table** by clicking on the small circle to the left of it. The circle will be filled in with a black dot to show that you have selected it. Fill in the correct columns to identify where the data is located. For example, if you want to make a pie chart of the Doctoral degree data, C5 (School2) has the categories and C6 (Number2) has the number of Doctoral degrees awarded in 2012. Fill in the screen as follows: **Categorical variable**: C5 School2 and **Summary variables**: C6 Number2. (Fig. 1-12)

Fig. I-I2

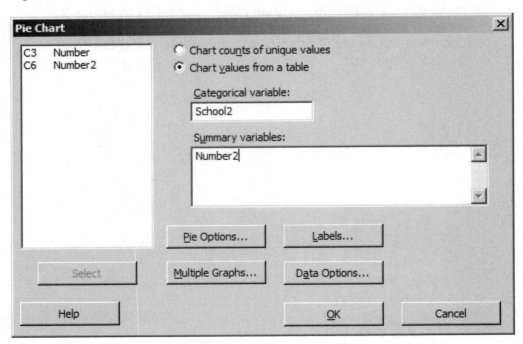

Click on **Labels** and enter an appropriate title. (Fig. 1-13)

• •

Fig. I-I3

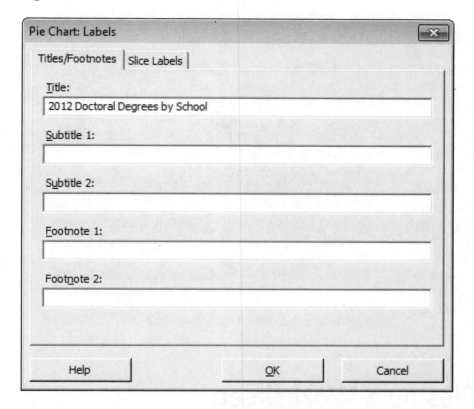

Click on the **Slice Labels** tab, and select **Category Name,** select **Frequency** and **Draw a line from label to slice** by clicking on the check boxes. Click on **OK** to view the pie chart. (Fig. 1-14) To print the chart or to copy it into your Word document, use the same procedure as described for the bar charts.

Fig. 1-14

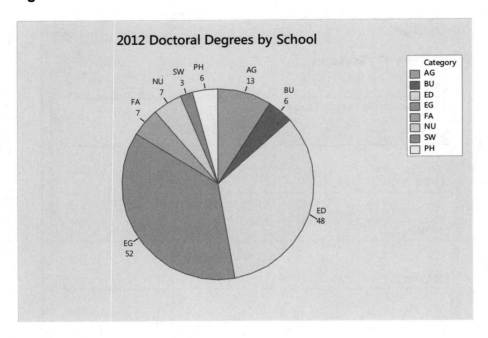

Closing a Worksheet:

When you have finished using a dataset (worksheet) you should close it. To do this, the Data Worksheet Window must be active. Just click anywhere in the worksheet to make it your active window. Then click on **FILE** and choose **Close Worksheet**. You will now have a clean Worksheet to begin another example.

Assignment

• •

Please answer all questions in the space provided. When you have completed this assignment, tear the pages along the perforation. Include with this assignment all computer work that is required to answer the questions. Each graph must be labeled with a title, axis labels, and a footnote with your name and section number. If the assignment requires you to print the Session Window, click on the Session Window and type your name and section number so you can identify your printout.

1. In this lesson you have learned two different graphical techniques for displaying qualitative data - the bar chart and the pie chart. When presenting data graphically you can choose between the two techniques. Sometimes one chart is more appealing than the other. For this example, the data you will be displaying is enrollment data by ethnicity for a particular school at a university. The data is stored in the files ETHNIC1.MTW, ETHNIC2.MTW, ETHNIC3.MTW, ETHNIC4.MTW .

   a. Do a simple bar chart using C3 (Number) as the Graph variable and C1 (Ethnicity) as the Categorical variable. Be sure to include appropriate labels (title, axis labels, and a footnote with your name and section.)

   b. Do a pie chart using C1 for the categories and C3 for the Summary variable. Label the pie slices using the percent option. Be sure to use an appropriate title.

   c. Which chart do you prefer and why?

   d. What do these graphs tell you about the ethnicity of the student body? Be specific and include at least four facts that you learned from the chart.

Note: Be sure to either print the graphs or copy them to a Word document.

2. For this example, you will use the file School.MTW. The data contained in this file is enrollment data by school within a university for the years 1990, 2000 and 2010.

    a. Do a simple bar chart for the 1990 data.

        Which school had the highest enrollment in 1990?
        _____

        How many students enrolled in the School of Engineering in 1990?_____

    b. Do a pie chart for the 2000 data. Enter an appropriate title. Label the pie slices using the category name and the percent option.

        What percentage of the students enrolled in the School of Education? _____

    c. Do a clustered bar chart for the entire data set clustering by SCHOOL. In order to do this, you must combine the 1990, 2000 and 2010 data using Cut & Paste.

        Which school had the highest enrollment during this time period? _____

        Which year had the highest enrollment for the School of Nursing? _____

        How many student nurses were there in that year? _____

        Describe the overall trend during these years for the School of Engineering.

        Compare the overall trends for the Schools of Engineering and Business.

Compare the overall trends among the 6 schools. Include at least four facts that you learned from the graphs.

Note: Be sure to either print the graphs or copy them to a Word document.

3. For this example you will use the file FACULTY1.MTW. The data contained in this file is the number of faculty by school for the years 1970, 1990, and 2010.

   a. Do a clustered bar chart for the data set clustering by School.

      In 1970, which school had the most faculty members?
      _____

      Did any school show a continuous increase in faculty throughout the period? If so, which school? _____

      Which school added the most faculty members between 1970 and 1990? _____

      What is the total number of faculty at this university in 1990.
      _____

      Which school had the greatest difference between their peak and lowest number of faculty? _____

Note: Be sure to either print the graph or copy it into a Word document.

Chapter 2

Quantitative Data Analysis

Much of the data that we collect is numerical, or quantitative data. Simply looking at a list of data points without organizing it in some way will not give us much information. So, particularly if the data set is large, we need techniques that we can use to summarize the data in order to get a better understanding of the data set. There are a variety of graphical techniques that are available that give excellent pictures of data sets. There are also some basic measurements of central tendency and of variation that are useful statistics to use when we are summarizing a data set. (We will study these measurements in the next chapter.) Let's begin by looking at some of the graphical techniques.

Histograms:

A histogram is very similar to the bar chart that you studied in the previous lesson. The main difference is that in a histogram the data is grouped into numerical categories instead of non-numerical categories. A histogram gives you a snapshot of the data set. From this snapshot you can begin to study the distribution of the data set. Does the data appear to be symmetric or does it appear to be skewed to the left or to the right? Does the data appear to be mound-shaped (normally distributed) or does it look bimodal? When working with very small datasets, these questions about the shape of a data set can be difficult to answer. So, let's begin with two fairly large data sets, each with 100 observations. The file is named **SAT.MTW**.

To open the file, click on: FILE → OPEN WORKSHEET

On the screen that appears, you must tell MINITAB that the worksheet is in the **Data Sets 4e** folder. Search through the folder for the **SAT.MTW** file. Once you open the file, the spreadsheet in the data window should contain the Math, Verbal and Writing SAT scores in columns C1, C2 and C3 for students accepted into the engineering program at a local university. Let's begin to analyze this data set by constructing histograms for each set of scores.

To do this, click on GRAPH → HISTOGRAM

On the pop-up screen that appears, double-click on a **Simple** histogram icon in the upper left corner of the pop-up screen. This should bring you to the main histogram screen. (Fig. 2-1)

• •
Fig. 2-1

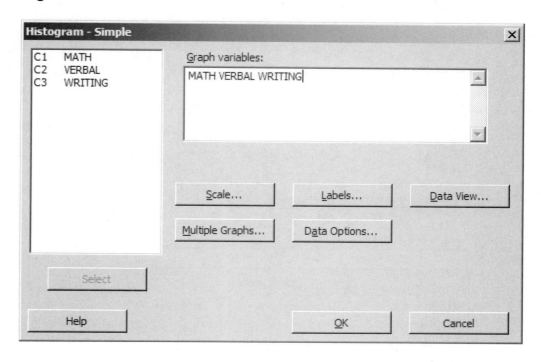

Suppose we are interested in comparing the three histograms. First select Math, Verbal and Writing scores for the **Graph Variables** by double-clicking on them in the rectangle at the left of the pop-up. We can do this comparison most easily if the histograms are drawn using the same X and Y scales. To do this, click on the button labeled **Multiple Graphs.** On the screen that appears, choose **On separate graphs** by clicking on the circle for that choice. Then choose **Same Y** and **Same X, including same bins** by clicking on the boxes for these choices. Click on **OK**.

The next step is to put a title on the histograms. Click on the **Labels** button. This **title** will appear on all three histograms. For example, you might choose the title: **SAT SCORES**. For the **Footnote**, enter your name and section number. Click on **OK.** This closes the pop-up and returns to the main histogram page. Then click on **OK** and the histograms will be produced. (Fig. 2-2). Make sure that the title, your name and section number appear on the graphs. Also, make sure the histograms have the same X and Y scales. If you are satisfied with the way the histograms look you close each of the graphs. (Your Data Window will now appear.)

· ·

Fig. 2-2

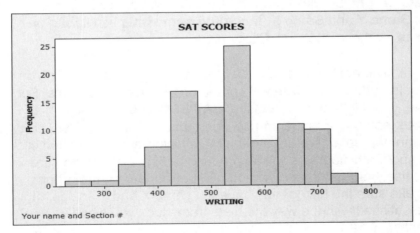

What do these histograms tell you about the SAT Scores? First, you should notice the shapes. The Math SAT histogram is slightly skewed to the left. The other two histograms are more mound-shaped. It also looks as if the centers of the Math SAT scores and

Verbal Sat scores are both higher than the center of the Writing SAT scores. The Writing SAT scores have a high concentration of scores around 550.

Boxplots:

Another useful graphical technique is the Boxplot. Let's construct boxplots for the three data sets of SAT scores.

To construct boxplots, click on: GRAPH → BOXPLOT

On the pop-up screen that appears, under the heading **Multiple Y's**, double-click on the **Simple** boxplot icon (in the lower left corner of the pop-up screen). This should bring you to the main boxplot screen. (Fig. 2-3)

Fig. 2-3

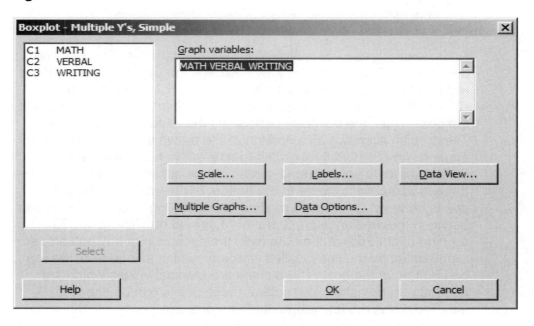

Next, click on the button **Labels**, and enter a **title** of SAT SCORES and put your name and section number as a **Footnote**.
Click on OK to close that Window and then click on OK again to produce the Boxplots. (Fig. 2-4)

Fig. 2-4

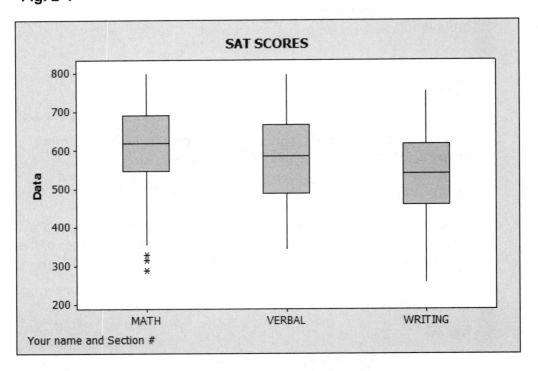

Each boxplot gives you a nice picture of the data set. The plot divides the data into four parts - the lower quartile, the upper quartile and the two middle quartiles. The box itself is drawn using the first quartile (Q1) as the bottom of the box and the third quartile (Q3) as the top of the box. Thus, the box itself represents the middle 50% of the data. The median is shown as a horizontal line drawn inside the box. If the median line is drawn through the middle of the box, then the middle 50% of the data set is evenly spread out on either side of the median. If the median line is closer to the bottom of the box, then the data points between Q1 and the median fall closer together and the points between the median and Q3 are more spread out. The lower 25% and the upper 25% of the data (with the exception of any outliers) are represented by the lines, called whiskers, which extend from the top and bottom of the box. The outliers are unusual values which are flagged with an asterisk (*) so that these points can be checked. MINITAB uses the following criteria for outliers:

A data point is considered an outlier if it is smaller than the *lower fence*.

(The lower fence is Q1 - 1.5 * (Q3 – Q1).)

A data point is also considered an outlier if it is larger than the *upper fence*.

(The upper fence is Q3 + 1.5 * (Q3 – Q1).)

All unusual values should be verified to be sure that a data entry error did not occur.

Close the current worksheet by clicking anywhere in the Worksheet Window and then clicking on the **"X"** in the upper right corner of the Window.

Dotplots:

• •

Dotplots are very useful when the data sets you have are small. Suppose we are interested in looking at the statistics for a Women's Collegiate Basketball team, and we have data on the number of points scored per game for the five starting players for last season. The data is contained in a file named **WOMENBB.MTW.** Open the file. You should have a data set with five columns of data (each column represents an individual player). To graphically compare the points scored for each player, we will use dotplots.

To construct the dotplots, click on: GRAPH→ DOTPLOT

On the pop-up screen that appears, double-click on the **Simple** dotplot for **Multiple Y's** icon in the lower left corner of the pop-up screen. This should bring you to the main dotplot screen. (Fig. 2-5)

In the window that appears, for **Graph Variables**, select all five columns. In order to compare the five players, it is very important that the dotplots are set up using the same scale. MINITAB does this automatically. Next, click on the **Labels** button, and enter an appropriate **Title** and enter your name and section number in the **Footnote** field, and then click on **OK.**

Fig. 2-5

Click on OK to view the dotplots. (Fig. 2-6)

Fig. 2-6

You may want to adjust the tick marks on the X-axis to make it easier to read the values. Double click anywhere on the numerical values of the X-axis. Click on the **Scale** tab for the X-axis. Click on **Position of ticks** and enter 2 : 35 / 2. This tells MINITAB that you want a tick label from 2 to 35 in steps of 2.

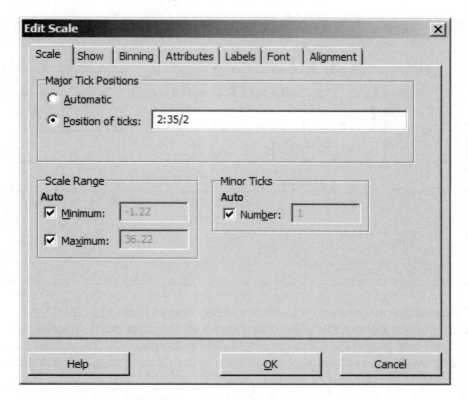

Click on OK to view the new plots. (Fig. 2-7)

Fig. 2-7

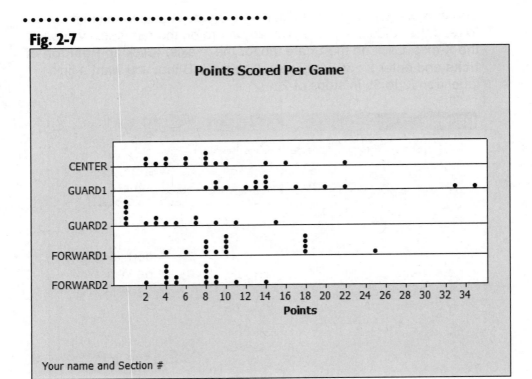

These dotplots give you a quick and easy way of looking at the five players simultaneously. The dots represent the data points (points scored per game) for each game played by the player. The values along the X-axis represent the number of points scored, and the dots represent the number of times a player scored that many points. For example, the dotplot for FORWARD2 shows that she scored 2 points in one game – there is 1 dot above the 2 on the X-axis. FORWARD2 also scored 4 points in 4 games, 5 points in 2 games and 8 points in four games. Since the scales are the same for all five plots, it is very simple to compare the points socred by each player.

Stem and Leaf Displays:

A stem-and-leaf display is the last of the graphical techniques that we will look at in this lesson. It is another way of getting a picture of the data set. It is different from the other graphs in that the stem-and-leaf display actually displays the raw data (in its original form or in a rounded form). In a stem-and-leaf the data is displayed in numerical order.

Chapter 2: Quantitative Data Analysis

Let's begin by looking at a set of test scores from a midterm exam in an Elementary Statistics course with 50 students. To do this, open the file named **MIDTERM.MTW.** In your Data Window, you should have one column of data labeled SCORES. This is the data that you will use to construct the stem-and-leaf.

When constructing stem-and-leaf displays, the graphs will appear as part of the Session Window. When you complete this lesson and print your Session Window, the stem-and-leaf displays will be part of your printout. Or, you can highlight and copy the Stem-and-Leaf in your Session Window and paste it into a Word document.

Click on: GRAPH → STEM-AND-LEAF

In the window that appears, for **Graph Variables,** double-click on C1. Then click on **OK** to view the stemplot in the Session Window. You may have to **Maximize** your Session Window and scroll up or down to see the entire stemplot. (Fig. 2-8)

A stem-and-leaf display is meant to give a quick overview of the data. It is not a sophisticated chart that you would see in magazines or newspapers. In the MINITAB display, the first column on the left is a counter. (This column counts the number of data points from the smallest value up to the median, and then counts down to the largest data value.) The stems are the next column of numbers. The leaves are the numbers to the right of the stems. The data itself is separated into these two parts: the stem and the leaf.

• •

Fig. 2-8

```
MINITAB - Untitled - [Session]
File  Edit  Data  Calc  Stat  Graph  Editor  Tools  Window  Help


Stem-and-Leaf Display: SCORES

Stem-and-leaf of SCORES  N  = 50
Leaf Unit = 1.0


   2    4   22
   7    4   57789
   9    5   04
  15    5   689999
  20    6   00223
  20    6
  23    7   134
  (7)   7   5678999
  20    8   022334444
  11    8   56678
   6    9   03
   4    9   569
   1   10   0
```

```
Welcome to Minitab, press F1 for help.                              Editable      10:57 AM
```

In this data set, notice that the stems range from 4 to 10. In the first row of the display you see: 4 22. This represents two data points: 42 and 42. *(The number 2 in the first column is the cumulative counter. This '2' tells us that there is a total of 2 data values in the first row.)* The second row of the display represents five points: 45,47,47,48 and 49. (Notice that the counter on the left shows "7", which represents the total of seven data points that are contained in the first two rows of the display.) This stemplot gives a clear picture of the shape of the data, which appears to be bimodal.

Assignment

• •

Please answer all questions in the space provided. When you have completed this assignment, tear the pages along the perforation. Include with this assignment all computer work that is required to answer the questions. Each graph must be labeled with a title, axis labels, and a footnote with your name and section number. If the assignment requires you to print the Session Window, click in the Session Window and type your name and section number so you can identify your printout.

1. For this example, you will use the file FINAL1.MTW. This large data set contains the final grades for two Introductory Statistics classes.

    a. Create a pair of histograms using the same scale. Be sure to label the graph with appropriate titles, footnotes, and axis labels. Maximize and print each histogram.

    b. Write a paragraph comparing and describing the two distributions of grades. Be sure to discuss shape (mound-shaped, skewed, bimodal), spread (max and min), and central tendencies.

Note: Be sure to either print the graphs or copy them to a Word document.

2. For this example, you will use the file REBOUND1.MTW. This file contains the number of rebounds per game for five starting players on a leading Women's basketball team.

    a. Do a set of dotplots on the same scale to display the data. Edit the X-scale so that the values on the scale are displayed in intervals of 2.

b. Write a paragraph summarizing the data. Discuss similarities and differences among the players. Be sure to consider the positions played.

Note: Be sure to either print the graph or copy it to a Word ocument.

3. For this example, you will use the file BBSCORE1.MTW. The file contains points scored by the winners and by the losers and the point spread for 19 different games last season. (Notice that point spread equals Winning Score - Losing Score.)

a. Construct a stem-and-leaf display of the point spread data (C3).

The data values range from a minimum of ___1___ to a maximum of ___99___.

What data values are represented by the second row of the stemplot? ~~15 18~~ 8, 9

Looking at the stemplot, you would conclude that most often the point spread was between ___15___ and ___18___.

Looking at the stemplot, determine the number of games in which the point spread was less than 20 points? ___11___

Do any data points look like possible outliers? _____
Which ones? _____

b. Do a boxplot of C3 to see if the "possible outliers" actually appear as outliers. What did you discover?

c. From the boxplot, approximate the following data values:

Median _____
First quartile _____   Third quartile _____   IQR _____
Minimum data value _____
Maximum data value _____

Move your cursor anywhere inside the Boxplot to confirm your values for the median, q1 and q3.

d. Construct two boxplots on the same page to compare the points scored by the Winners, C1, to the points scored by the Losers, C2.

e. From the boxplot for the Winners, fill in the following information:

Highest Score _____   Lowest Score _____
First quartile _____   Third quartile _____   IQR _____

25% of the time, the Winners scored more than _____ points.

25% of the time, the Winners scored less than _____ points.

Find the cutoff points for the middle 50%:
Winners scored between _____ and _____ points.

f. From the boxplot for the Losers, fill in the following information:

75% of the time, the Losers scored fewer than _____ points.

25% of the time, the Losers scored more than _____ points.

Note: Be sure to either print the graphs or copy them to a Word document. For the Stem-and-Leaf Display, you can print the Session Window or highlight the Stem-and-Leaf plot and paste it into your Word document.

Chapter 3

Measures of Central Tendency And Variation

The graphical methods for representing data that you studied in the previous lessons are very useful techniques for organizing data. As you have probably discovered, it is very difficult to get any useful information from a list of numbers. An organized display of the data set is much more informative. In addition to the graphical techniques, there are some basic measurements that can be calculated from the data set. These measurements describe the data set by using two key characteristics - central tendency and variation.

Central Tendency

One statistic that measures the center of a data set is the average or MEAN. Everyone is familiar with this measurement. It is calculated by adding all the data points in the set and dividing by the number of data points in the set. Another statistic that measures the center is the MEDIAN. The median divides the data set in half - 50% of the data points have values less than or equal to the median and 50% of the data points have values greater than or equal to the median.

You might ask why there are two different measures of the center of a data set. To answer this question, let's create three small data sets. We will enter the data directly into a MINITAB worksheet.

In the Data Window, enter the following data points into Column 1:

1 2 3 4 5 6 7 8 9 10

Enter the following data points into Column 2:

1 2 3 4 5 6 7 8 9 25

Enter the following data points into Column 3:

1 2 3 4 5 6 7 8 9 100

Give each column a name by placing the cursor in the box directly below the column heading. Under C1 type "Trial 1"; under C2 type "Trial 2" and under C3 type "Trial 3".
(Fig. 3-1)

• •

Fig. 3-1

Let's compare the means and medians for these three columns. To do this, click on:

STAT → BASIC STATISTICS → DISPLAY DESCRIPTIVE STATISTICS

In the screen that appears, highlight all three columns and click on **SELECT.** These three columns will appear in the box entitled **VARIABLES.** Click on **OK.** (Fig. 3-2)

• •

Fig. 3-2

The following information should appear in the Session Window: (Fig. 3-3)

• •

Fig. 3-3

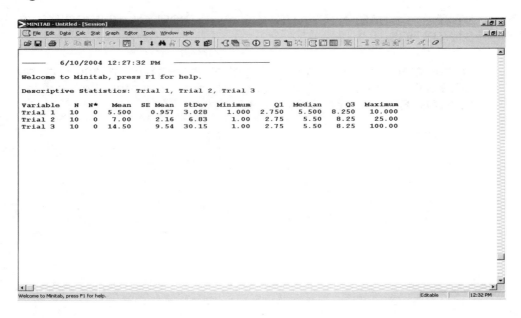

Notice the values of the mean and median for the three columns of data. The median is 5.50 for all 3 columns of data. This means that, in each data set, 50% of the observations are less than or equal to 5.50 and 50% of the observations are greater than or equal to 5.50.

Now look at the mean. It jumps from 5.50 to 7.00 and then to 14.50. In each case the jumps are caused by one unusual data point (a probable outlier). It is important to note that, particularly in small data sets, an outlier can have a significant impact on the value of the mean. The "average" person thinks of the mean as the middle of the data set. This can lead to some misunderstandings. The mean is the average of the set of data points, but it might not fall at the 50 % mark of the data set. The median is the measurement that always falls at the 50 % mark in the data set. It is a better measure of the center for data sets containing extreme values.

Variation:

· ·

The second key piece of information that is needed to describe a data set is a measure of the variation in the data set. One way to measure variation is to calculate the RANGE. The Range is: MAX - MIN. Another statistic used to calculate variation is called the STANDARD DEVIATION. The standard deviation is a measure of the "average" deviation of the data points around the mean. A "small" standard deviation indicates that the data is clustered close to the mean. A "large" standard deviation indicates that the data is more widely dispersed. The terms "large" and "small" are used in relation to the actual values in the data set. For example, a standard deviation of 100 would be considered "large" in a data set with a mean of 150. In a data set with a mean of 5000, a standard deviation of 100 would be considered "small."

Look at the Session Window (Fig. 3-3) that contains the Descriptive Statistics for Trial 1, Trial 2 and Trial 3. The standard deviation for the Trial 1 data is 3.028. This means that the "average" deviation of the data points from the mean is 3.028. Now look at the standard deviations for Trial 2 and Trial 3. Notice how the standard deviation increases. This means that these two data sets have more variability. In this example, the increased variability is due to the outliers. So, when comparing data sets, the larger standard deviation indicates that a data set has more variability.

Since we are finished with this data, close the worksheet by clicking anywhere in the Data Window to activate it, and then choosing **Close Worksheet** from the **File** menu.

Using the Mean and Standard Deviation: Empirical Rule: For Normally Distributed Data

How can we make use of both the mean and standard deviation of a data set? We can combine these two key characteristics to get an idea of the distribution of the data. How we use these characteristics to describe the data set depends on the information we have regarding the shape of the data. If we use a histogram, stem-and leaf or dotplot to graph the data and see that the data is mound-shaped then we can make the following three statements (called the Empirical Rule) about the data set:

a. Approximately 68% of the data is contained in the interval:
$(\bar{x} \pm 1s)$.

b. Approximately 95% of the data is contained in the interval:
$(\bar{x} \pm 2s)$.

c. Approximately 100% of the data is contained in the interval:
$(\bar{x} \pm 3s)$.

As an example, let's look at the SAT.MTW data set. This data set contains MATH, VERBAL and WRITING SAT scores. For this example, we will use the WRITING scores. First, construct a histogram of the data, (GRAPH → HISTOGRAM). You should notice from your histogram that the data looks fairly mound-shaped with no unusual values and no extreme skewness. Now that you have seen a display of the data set, close the Graph Window by clicking on the X in the upper right corner.

Find the mean and standard deviation of the data by using:

STAT → BASIC STATISTICS → DISPLAY DESCRIPTIVE STATISTICS

The mean is 536.0 and the standard deviation is 104.0.

The following steps are used to calculate the $[\bar{x} \pm 1s]$, $[\bar{x} \pm 2s]$, and $[\bar{x} \pm 3s]$ intervals in MINITAB. (A hand calculator can also be used for these calculations.) First, calculate the value for the lower limit: $[\bar{x} - 1s]$. To do this, click on:

CALC → CALCULATOR

In the screen that appears, you will **Store result in variable** C4. In the box for **Expression** type: 536 - 104. Click on **OK.** Your result, 432, should appear in C4. Now, calculate the value for the upper limit: $[\bar{x} + 1s]$. To do this, return to the Calculator screen. This time **store result in variable** C5, and the **Expression** is 536 + 104. Click on **OK.** Your result, 640, should appear in C5.

You can now use this information to make the following statement about the data:

"Approximately 68% of the Writing SAT Scores fall between 432 and 640."

Now repeat the procedure to calculate $[\bar{x} - 2s]$ and $[\bar{x} + 2s]$. For $[\bar{x} - 2s]$, **store result in variable** C6, and type the **Expression:** 536 - 2*104. For $[\bar{x} + 2s]$, **store result in variable** C7 and type the **Expression:** 536 + 2*104. These numbers (in C6 and C7) represent the $[\bar{x} \pm 2s]$ interval and can be used in the following statement:

"Approximately 95% of the Writing SAT scores lie between 328 and 744."

Finally repeat the procedure to calculate $[\bar{x} - 3s]$ and $[\bar{x} + 3s]$ and **store results in variable** C8 and C9. These numbers represent the $[\bar{x} \pm 3s]$ interval and can be used in the following statement:

"Approximately 100% of the Writing SAT scores lie between 224 and 846."

Let's look at the data and see how well the Empirical Rule works. Determine how many data points actually do fall in the intervals that we created. Let's begin with the $[\bar{x} \pm 3s]$ interval and see how many data points are in this interval. It would be rather difficult to answer this question with the data as it appears in C3. It would be much easier to look at the data in numerical order. To do this, click on:

DATA → SORT

In the screen that appears, the **Sort column** is C3 Writing and the **By Column:** is also C3 Writing. (Note: MINITAB assumes the sort order is ascending unless you select the **descending** check box.) Below the heading **Store sorted data in,** select **Columns of current worksheet** and type in C10. (Fig. 3-4)

· ·
Fig. 3-4

The Empirical Rule states that approximately 100% of the data lies between 224 and 846. Look through the ordered set of data (C10) by moving the down arrow on the right side of the Data Window. There are no data points, outside the interval (224 - 846). So, the Empirical Rule is correct. (100% of the data falls within the interval which is what the Empirical Rule states).

How many data points fall outside the interval [$\bar{x} \pm 2s$], (328 - 744)? There are two points: 745 and 753. So, 98 out of 100, or 98%, of the data actually lies within the [$\bar{x} \pm 2s$] interval. The Empirical Rule states that approximately 95% of the data should lie in this interval. So, the Empirical Rule's estimate is a good estimate of what actually did occur.

Lastly, how many points fall outside the interval [$\bar{x} \pm 1s$], (432 - 640)? There are 30 points: Data points numbered #1 - 14 and # 85 - 100. So 70% of the data is contained in the interval [$\bar{x} \pm 1s$]. Again, the Empirical Rule, which states that approximately 68% of the data should fall in the interval [$\bar{x} \pm 1s$], works well.

We have just verified the Empirical Rule by calculating the percentages of the sample data which fall within 1, 2, and 3 standard deviations of the mean. Using only the mean and standard deviation of a sample, the Empirical Rule can be used to describe the distribution of the whole population.

Chebyshev's Rule: For Non-normally Distributed Data

Now, let's consider a data set that is not mound shaped. If the data set is not mound shaped, the Empirical Rule does not apply. There is another rule, called Chebyshev's Rule that can be utilized. This rule states that "at least $(1 - \frac{1}{k^2})$ of the data will lie in the interval $[\bar{x} \pm ks]$", where k = # of standard deviations and s = sample standard deviation.

For example, suppose we would like to make a statement about the proportion of the data that lies within **2** standard deviations of the mean. Then $k = 2$ and the rule states that at least $(1 - \frac{1}{2^2})$ or $\frac{3}{4}$ of the data lies within the $[\bar{x} \pm 2s]$ interval. To calculate the proportion of the data that lies within a given number (k) of standard deviations around the mean, simply replace the k with the appropriate value and calculate the fraction $(1 - \frac{1}{k^2})$.

Notice the difference between the two rules - the Empirical and Chebyshev's. If you look at the $[\bar{x} \pm 2s]$ interval, the Empirical Rule states that "approximately 95% of the data lies in that interval". Chebyshev's Rule states that "at least 75% of the data lies in that interval". It is important that you use the correct rule for the given data set. This can be determined by graphing the data. If the data appears relatively mound shaped, then the Empirical Rule should be used. If it does not look mound shaped, then Chebyshev's Rule should be used. Thus, using only the mean, the standard deviation and one of these rules, you can get a general idea of the interval in which you can expect most of your data to fall.

Close the Data Window since we are finished with this data.

Standardizing a data set:

Often, when analyzing data, it is necessary to compare data sets that have different means and standard deviations. For example, suppose you want to compare EXAM 1 and EXAM 2 grades in an Introductory Statistics course. The data is stored in a file named STANDARD.MTW. Open this worksheet.

Find the mean and standard deviation for each set of Exam scores. To do this, click on:

STAT → BASIC STATISTICS → DISPLAY DESCRIPTIVE STATISTICS

In the window that appears select the **Variables** C1 and C2 and click on **OK.** Notice that the means and standard deviations differ for the two exams.

How can we compare the observations in the two data sets? One way to make comparisons is to standardize the data sets. Standardizing a data set is done by using the following formula:

$$Z = \frac{X - \overline{X}}{S}$$

Each observation, X, is converted to a standardized value, Z. To do this in MINITAB, click on:

CALC → STANDARDIZE

In the screen that appears, the columns you are **standardizing** are C1 and C2 so select both of them as **Input columns. Store the results** in two empty columns, C3 and C4. The standardizing formula we are using is **Subtract mean and divide by standard deviation.** Make sure that the correct choice is selected at the bottom of the pop-up. (Fig. 3-5)

· ·
Fig. 3-5

C3 and C4 now contain the standardized data. Standardized data sets all have the same mean (0.00) and the same standard deviation (1.00). Verify this for C3 and C4 by using:

STAT → BASIC STATISTICS → DISPLAY DESCRIPTIVE STATISTICS.

Now suppose that you are Person # 4 in the data set (Fig. 3-6). You scored 87 on the first exam and 80 on the second exam. On which of the two exams did you receive a higher grade relative to the rest of the class? To answer this question, look at your standardized scores of .22713 and .29580 (Fig. 3-6). The larger value indicates the higher score so your Exam 2 grade was actually better, relatively speaking.

● ●

Fig. 3-6

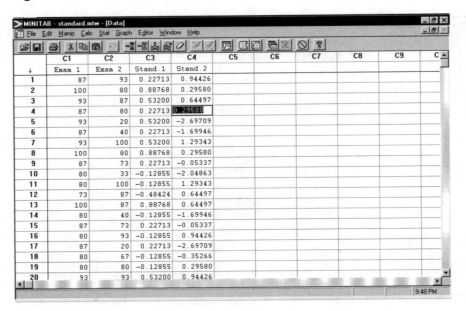

	C1	C2	C3	C4	C5	C6	C7	C8	C9	C
	Exam 1	Exam 2	Stand.1	Stand.2						
1	87	93	0.22713	0.94426						
2	100	80	0.88768	0.29580						
3	93	87	0.53200	0.64497						
4	87	80	0.22713	0.29580						
5	93	20	0.53200	-2.69709						
6	87	40	0.22713	-1.69946						
7	93	100	0.53200	1.29343						
8	100	80	0.88768	0.29580						
9	87	73	0.22713	-0.05337						
10	80	33	-0.12855	-2.04863						
11	80	100	-0.12855	1.29343						
12	73	87	-0.48424	0.64497						
13	100	87	0.88768	0.64497						
14	80	40	-0.12855	-1.69946						
15	87	73	0.22713	-0.05337						
16	80	93	-0.12855	0.94426						
17	87	20	0.22713	-2.69709						
18	80	67	-0.12855	-0.35266						
19	80	80	-0.12855	0.29580						
20	93	93	0.53200	0.94426						

Assignment

· ·

Please answer all questions in the space provided. When you have completed this assignment, tear the pages along the perforation. Include with this assignment all computer work that is required to answer the questions. Each graph must be labeled with a title, axis labels, and a footnote with your name and section number. If the assignment requires you to print the Session Window, click in the Session Window and type your name and section number so you can identify your printout.

1. For this example, you will use the file BASEBALL1.MTW. This file contains the 2011 salaries for two major league baseball teams. C1 contains the salaries for one randomly selected MLB team, and C2 contains the salaries for a second randomly selected team.

   a. Use MINITAB to calculate the mean, median and standard deviation for the salaries for each team.

TEAM1	TEAM2
Team:	Team:
Mean:	Mean:
Median:	Median:
Standard Deviation:	Standard Deviation:

   b. Which measure of central tendency, the mean or the median, do you think would give a more realistic picture of the salaries? Write an explanation justifying your choice.

   c. Use the means, medians and standard deviations of the two data sets to compare the two teams. Include comments on similarities and differences in salaries.

2. Construct a stem-and-leaf display of the salaries for TEAM1.

   a. Describe the shape of the distribution of the salaries.

   b. Calculate the interval $[\bar{x} \pm 2s]$. Using the appropriate rule, Empirical or Chebyshev's, make a statement about the percentage of the players' salaries that you would expect to fall within this interval.

3. Suppose you are interested in determining how well the highest paid player is paid relative to the rest of the players on his team. For each team, convert all the players' salaries into standardized scores. Locate the highest paid player from each team.

   Team1 salary:_____   Team2 salary:
   _____

   Z-score: _____   Z-score: _____

   Compare the standardized scores for these two players. Who is the higher paid player relative to the rest of his team? Explain your conclusion.

Chapter 3: Measures of Central Tendency and Variation

4. For this example, you will use the COLLEGE1.MTW file. This file contains Math, Verbal and Writing SAT scores.

   a. Construct a histogram for the Math SAT scores. Be sure to include a title, X and Y axis labels, your name and your section.

   b. Describe the shape of the distribution.

   c. Calculate the mean and standard deviation of the Math scores.

   d. Calculate the intervals $[\bar{x} \pm 1s]$, $[\bar{x} \pm 2s]$, $[\bar{x} \pm 3s]$. What percentage of the data would you expect to fall within each of these intervals? (You can use MINITAB or a hand calculator to calculate the intervals.)

(handwritten)

68% → in 1st interval

$\bar{x} \pm 1s$
583.63 ± 48.51
$(535.12), 632.14)$

$\bar{x} \pm 2s$
$583.63 \pm 2(48.51$
$(486.61, 680.65)$

99.7% → $\bar{x} \pm 3s$
583.63 ± 48.51

$(438.1, 729.16)$

95% in 2nd interval

   e. Organize the data set into numerical order. What percentage of the data set actually did fall within the interval $[\bar{x} \pm 2s]$? List the data points that did not lie in the interval.

95% fell inside
5% fell outside

$465, 480, 738, 690, 684$

   f. Compare the means and standard deviations of the Math, Verbal and Writing SAT scores. On average, on which of the two parts of the SAT test do students do better? Math + writing Which set of scores has more variability? Math Which set had the lowest score? Writing Which set had the highest score? Math 738
   449.

51

Chapter 4

Probability and Simulation

Mathematical models have been used to describe real-world problems for centuries. Today, with the use of high speed computers, mathematical models have become more and more sophisticated and it is now possible to model very complex problems. We use mathematical models in statistics to describe random events, which are events whose outcomes vary. These models are called probability models or probability distributions.

A simple example of a random event is the roll of a die. When the die is rolled, the possible outcomes are the numbers 1 to 6. If the die is fair, each outcome is equally likely and has probability of $\frac{1}{6}$. This means that, even though any individual outcome is random, the long run outcome is predictable. This information can be displayed in a table, called a probability distribution, where X = the number rolled and P(X) = it's probability.

• •

Fig. 4-I

X	P(X)
1	.167
2	.167
3	.167
4	.167
5	.167
6	.167

The probabilities in the above table are <u>theoretical probabilities.</u> These probabilities are determined from the physical characteristics of the die. Since the die is fair, each of the sides has an equal chance of occurring so the probabilities in the above table are all the same.

Simulating Equally Likely Events:
• •

We could also calculate <u>experimental probabilities</u> by "rolling" a fair die a large number of times. These experimental probabilities should closely agree with the probabilities in the theoretical model (Fig. 4-1).

Rather than actually rolling a die a large number of times, we will have MINITAB simulate the experiment. MINITAB will do this by randomly generating integers from 1 to 6 to represent the results of rolling a die. The random number generator will give each of the numbers, 1 to 6, an equal chance of occurring.

To do this, click on CALC → RANDOM DATA → INTEGER

In the screen that appears, **Generate** 100 rows, **Store in** C1, **Minimum value** is 1, **Maximum value** is 6. (Fig. 4-2)

• •

Fig. 4-2

The results of 100 random rolls of a fair die are in C1 in the Data Window. Let's compare these experimental results with our theoretical model. To do this, we need to count the number of 1's, 2's, 3's, etc. that are in C1.

Click on: STAT → TABLES→ TALLY INDIVIDUAL VARIABLES

In the screen that appears, select the **Variable** C1 and **Display counts** and **percents** by selecting the boxes to the left of these options.

In the Session Window, a table of **Summary Statistics** will appear. This table lists the possible values of the random variable, X. In our example, the values are the numbers 1 through 6, representing the rolls of a die. The next column in the table is a count of the number of times, in 100 tosses, that the different outcomes occurred. The final column is the percent of times that the different outcomes occurred. If you try this experiment, your results will not be identical to the results in this table because each simulation is different. (Fig. 4-3)

. . . .
Fig. 4-3

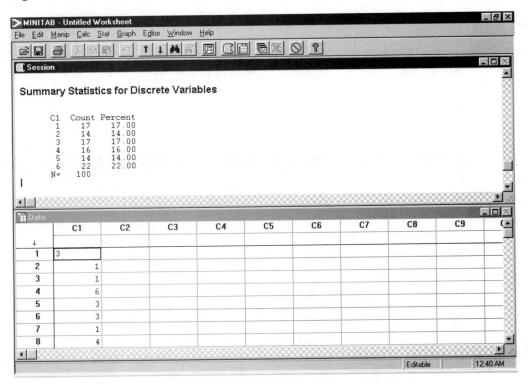

Compare the percentages in the Summary Table with the theoretical probabilities in Fig. 4-1. The theoretical probabilities and the experimental results should be close. As an example, look at the theoretical probability of rolling a "2" on a die. That's equal to .167. Now look at the experimental result for rolling a "2". In our example the result is 14% or .14. As you can see, these probabilities are not identical, but they are relatively close. The difference between them is due to randomness. An experiment with a limited number of trials (in this case, a limited number of rolls of the die), will not give the exact probabilities that are in the theoretical model.

The results of the experiment will tend to be closer to the theoretical model if the number of trials is increased. Let's see what happens if we roll a die 1000 times. Repeat the process using:

CALC → RANDOM DATA → INTEGER

Generate 1000 **rows** this time and **store results in** C2. Then create a new Summary Table. If you **Maximize** your Session Window and move the up arrow on the right side of your screen you can see the results of both experiments.
(Fig.4-4)

• •

Fig. 4-4

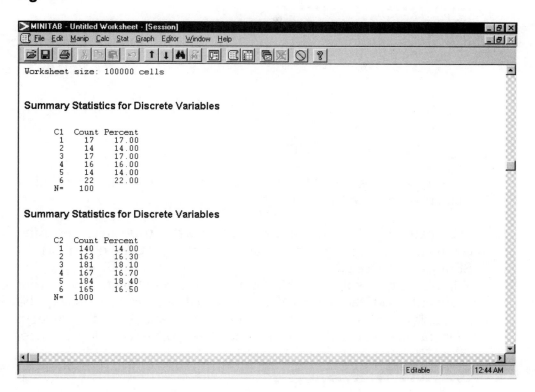

Notice that the probabilities in the larger experiment are becoming closer to the theoretical probabilities.

Simulating Events That Are Not Equally Likely:

• •

Suppose that the die we are using is a "loaded" die. The die is loaded so that a "1" will occur 50% of the time and the remaining 5 numbers will each occur 10% of the time. Simulating this experiment requires the use of a probability distribution because these events do not have equal probability. (In the previous example, when MINITAB generated the numbers 1 to 6, each number had an equal chance of occurring.)

The probability model for this experiment is the following:

• •

Fig. 4-5

X	P(X)
1	.500
2	.100
3	.100
4	.100
5	.100
6	.100

To simulate this in MINITAB, we need to enter the probability distribution into the Data Worksheet.

Let's begin by clearing the Data Worksheet. To do this, move the cursor to any location in the Data Worksheet. Click on: EDIT →
SELECT ALL CELLS
Now all the data should be highlighted. Press the **Delete** key on your keyboard, and the Data Window should be empty. Using the probability model in Figure 4-5, enter the values of the random variable, X, in C1 and enter the theoretical probabilities in C2. Label C1 as "X" and C2 as "P(X)". (Fig. 4-6)

• •

Fig. 4-6

Now simulate rolling this "loaded" die 100 times. To do this, click on:

CALC → RANDOM DATA → DISCRETE

In the screen that appears, **Generate** 100 **rows of data**, **Store in columns** C3, **Values in** C1 and **probabilities in** C2. Click on **OK.**

What appears in C3 in the Data Window are the results of 100 rolls of a loaded die. Let's again compare these experimental results with our theoretical model. To do this, we need a summary of the results in C3.

To do this, click on: STAT → TABLES → TALLY INDIVIDUAL VARIABLES. Select C3 as your variable.

Compare the theoretical probabilities (Fig. 4-5) in the model to your experimental results in your Session Window (Fig. 4-7). How close are they?

Now repeat the process again for 1000 "rolls" of the die and store the results in C4. Use STAT → TABLES → TALLY INDIVIDUAL VARIABLES to summarize the data in C4. Notice that the experimental probabilities (Fig. 4-7) are closer to the theoretical probabilities. (Fig. 4-5) Since this is random data, your results will not be exactly the same as those shown below.

• •

Fig. 4-7

When you have finished using a dataset (worksheet) you should close it. To do this, the Data Worksheet Window must be active. Just click anywhere in the worksheet to make it your active window. Then click on **FILE** and choose **Close Worksheet**. You will now have a clean Worksheet to begin another example.

Assignment

Please answer all questions in the space provided. When you have completed this assignment, tear the pages along the perforation. Include with this assignment all computer work that is required to answer the questions. Each graph must be labeled with a title, axis labels, and a footnote with your name and section number. If the assignment requires you to print the Session Window, click in the Session Window and type your name and section number so you can identify your printout.

1. The Birthday Paradox: Suppose you are in a room with 24 other people. You would like to answer the following question: What are the chances that at least two people in the room have the same birthday?

   a. Now that you know something about probability, take an "educated guess" at the chances that at least two people in the room have the same birthday. Write your answer here:

   This probability is difficult to calculate mathematically; however, it is an ideal simulation problem. Let's simulate the problem and see how closely your "guess" agrees with the simulated results.

   To run the simulation, begin with the following information:

   1. There are 365 days in a year. (We will ignore leap years).
   2. There are 25 people in the room. (You and 24 others).
   3. Each person could have any day of the year as his or her birthday, so each birthday is equally likely.

   Start your simulation with 1 room of 25 people:

   Click on: CALC → RANDOM DATA → INTEGER

   In the screen that appears, **Generate** 25 **rows of data** (representing the 25 people), **Store in column(s)** C1 (representing 1 room), **Minimum value** is 1 (representing January 1), **Maximum value** is 365 (representing December 31).

   The question is: Are there at least two people with the same birthday?

In other words, are there at least two numbers in C1 that are the same? The easiest way to answer this question is to summarize the data.

Click on: STAT → TABLES → TALLY INDIVIDUAL VARIABLES

On the screen that appears, select C1 and click on COUNTS. Next click on OK, and in the Session Window, you will see a summary table of C1. This table lists each of the different birthdays that occurred in this simulation, as well as a count of the number of people who had that birthday. Notice that most counts are 1's. If you see a count of "2" or more, then you have at least two people in the room with the same birthday.

b. Did you find at least one match in C1?

In order to calculate the probability of finding at least two people with the same birthday you must repeat this experiment several times.

You can generate several rooms with 25 people at the same time.

To do this, click on: CALC → RANDOM DATA → INTEGER

In the screen that appears, **Generate** 25 **rows of data, Store in columns** C2-C50, **Minimum value** is 1, **Maximum value** is 365.

You now have 49 more rooms with 25 people in each room. Now summarize each of the 50 columns so that you can look for matches (people with the same birthday). When you use STAT → TABLES → TALLY Individual Variable command, you can select C1-C50, and the summary tables for all 50 columns will appear in the Session Window.

c. Maximize the Session Window. The first set of column tallies that you see should be C1-C5. Look through the counts for each column to see whether you have a match in that column. A match will be a '2' or '3' in the count column indicating that 2 or 3 people have that same birthday. For C1 – C5, how many of the columns have a match? Record this number in the table below next to C1-C5. Scroll through the Session Window and repeat this process for the remaining columns.

Col1-Col5: __4__   Col 26-Col30: __3__

Col6-Col10: __2__   Col31-Col35: __2__

Col11-Col15: __1__   Col36-Col40: __3__

Col16-Col20: __2__   Col41-Col45: __3__

Col21-Col25: __2__   Col46-Col50: __5__

d. Of the 50 columns that you generated, how many of them had at least one matching pair?

e. Based on your simulation, what is the probability that, in a room with 25 people, at least 2 people have the same birthday?

Note: the probability is equal to (# of columns with a matching pair / 50)

f. How close is your experimental probability to the theoretical probability, which is .57?

2. In this example, you will simulate a popular dice game, called CRAPS. In the game, 2 dice are rolled and the sum is recorded. Here are the rules:

a. If a sum of 7 or 11 is rolled on the first roll, it's an automatic WINNER and the game is over.

b. If a sum of 2, 3, or 12 is rolled on the first roll, it's an automatic LOSER and the game is over.

c. If a sum of 4, 5, 6, 8, 9, or 10 is rolled on the first roll, that number becomes your "POINT" and the game CONTINUES until you roll your POINT again and WIN or you roll 7 and LOSE.

NOTE: A "7" is only a WINNER if it's the FIRST roll of the game. At any other time, it's a LOSER. An "11" is only a WINNER on the first roll of the game. At any other time, you ignore it and continue playing. A "2, 3, or 12" is only a LOSER on the first roll. At any other time, you ignore it and continue playing.

For example, suppose the following numbers represent 20 rolls of the dice.

4, 5, 12, 11, 4, 6, 3, 7, 7, 3, 11, 5, 6, 12, 3, 7, 2, 8, 11, 7

Using these rolls, your first roll is a "4" which is your POINT. (The game continues until you roll either a "4" and win or a "7" and lose. All other rolls simply continue the game.) Thus, your first game is: 4, 5, 12, 11, 4 and you WIN. Game2 begins with a roll of "6" and ends with the roll of a "7". You LOSE. Game3 starts and ends with the "7". You WIN since "7" is an automatic winner on the first roll. Game4 starts and ends with the "3". You LOSE since "3" is an automatic loser on the first roll. Game5 starts and ends with the "11". You WIN since "11" is an automatic winner on the first roll. Game6 starts with a "5" which is your POINT. (The game continues until you roll either a "5" and win or a "7" and lose. All other rolls simply continue the game.) Thus, your game is: 5, 6, 12, 3, 7 and you Lose. Game7 starts and ends with the "2". You LOSE since "2" is an automatic loser on the first roll. Game8 starts with an "8" which is your POINT. (The game continues until you roll either an "8" and win or a "7" and lose. All other rolls simply continue the game.) Thus, your game is: 8, 11, 7 and you Lose.

There are two different ways to do this simulation. One way would be to use the random number generator to roll one die and store the results in C1 and then roll the second die and store the results in C2. Then add the two columns together and store the results in C3. The second way is to use the probability distribution with X = the sum of the two dice and P(X) = the probability of each possible sum. We will use the probability distribution method.

Start with a New Worksheet and enter the probability distribution into C1 and C2.

• •

Fig. 4-8

X	P(X)
2	.028
3	.056
4	.083
5	.111
6	.139
7	.167
8	.139
9	.111
10	.083
11	.056
12	.028

These probabilities are based on the roll of a pair of dice. There are 36 possible ordered pairs of rolls. For example, the only way to get a sum of 2 is to roll the pair (1,1). Thus, the probability of rolling a sum of 2 is 1 out of 36, which is .028.

Now we will use the probability distribution to simulate 15 rolls of the dice and record the sums.

To do this, click on: CALC → RANDOM DATA → DISCRETE

Fill in the input screen with the appropriate information.

The results are in C3. (Fig. 4-9)

Fig. 4-9

Let's record the WINS and LOSSES for these 15 simulated rolls in C3:

Start with the first roll, "6", the first number in C3. If you look back at the rules, "6" is a POINT and the game continues until you either roll a "6" and win or roll a "7" and lose. The second roll, the second number in C3, is a "7", so you LOSE. This ends Game 1.

The first roll of the next game is "5", the third number in C3. 5 is your POINT and the game continues until you either roll a "5" and win, or you roll a "7" and lose. Look down C3 until you see either a 5 or a 7. This game ends with the roll of "7" so you LOSE. The rolls for this game were: 5, 9, 6, 8, 4, 4, 9, 7.

Game #3 starts and ends with a roll of "12", the 11th number in C3. Since "12" is an automatic LOSER on the first roll, you LOSE.

Game #4 starts and ends with a roll of "7", the 12th number in C3. Since "7" is an automatic WINNER on the first roll, you WIN.

Game #5 starts with "9" and ends with "7" and is a LOSER.

Game #6 starts and ends with "11" and is an automatic WINNER.

The games are summarized below:

Game Number	Rolls	Result
1	6,7	Loss
2	5,9,6,8,4,4,9,7	Loss
3	12	Loss
4	7	Win
5	9,7	Loss
6	11	Win

So, a total of 6 games were played with the results: 2 Winners and 4 Losers. So the winning percentage is 2 out of 6 or 33%.

Note: When you do your simulation, you may end up with an incomplete game at the end. Simply ignore that partial game.

a. Simulate 200 rolls of the two dice using the probability distribution in Fig. 4-8. Store the results in C3.

b. From the data pull-down menu, choose DATA → DISPLAYDATA and select C3. This will display your data in your Session Window.Highlight the data in your Session Window and print it out.

c. On the printout of the Session Window, reading across the row, circle each complete game and tally the Win's and Losses.

d. How many games did you WIN?

e. How many games did you LOSE?

f. What was your winning percentage?

.47

g. Compare your winning percentage to the theoretical probability of winning at CRAPS, which is 49.3%.

<47%

Note: Be sure to include the printout of your Craps Games.

Chapter 5

The Binomial Random Variable

You have learned that a random variable is a variable with a probability distribution associated with its set of possible outcome values. Some random variables have special names such as the BINOMIAL random variable and are well worth studying because knowledge of their probability distribution allows you to make important statistical inferences about a population based on a sample from this population.

The binomial random variable is one of the most important of all the random variables. Can you define what you mean when you say X is a binomial random variable? First of all, you must have a series of random trials (they are called binomial trials) satisfying all of the following conditions:

1. There are a fixed number of trials (n = number of trials).
2. All trials are independent.
3. There are two outcomes on each trial (success or failure).
4. There is a fixed probability of success on each trial
   (p = prob. of success).

If you let X = number of successes in n binomial trials, then X is a binomial random variable defined by the parameters n and p, where n is the number of trials and p is the probability of success on a trial.

For example, suppose we know that currently 22% of all adults in the U.S. smoke. Then p = .22 represents the proportion of individuals in the population who smoke. Also, p could be interpreted as the probability that a randomly selected individual smokes. You now select a sample of individuals from the population and count the number of individuals who smoke. Your outcome is a random binomial outcome with parameters n and p.

There are 3 important things that you will learn to do using MINITAB and the Binomial distribution:

1. If an experiment meets the conditions of a binomial model, then the model can be used to measure the likelihood (probability) of different outcomes. We can use MINITAB to calculate <u>any</u> binomial probability that we want. There are two ways to do this:

   a. Using the **probability distribution** option, MINITAB can calculate P(X = b), where b is a specific numerical outcome. This probability can be viewed in the Session Window, or saved in a column.

   b. Using the **cumulative probability distribution**, MINITAB can calculate   P(X ≤ b). Again, this can be viewed in the Session Window or saved in a column.

2. A binomial distribution is a _discrete_ distribution. Therefore, the appropriate graph to use for this distribution is a bar chart. The important thing to notice is the shape of the distribution. Recall that a binomial random variable is defined by n (number of trials) and p (probability of success). It is these two parameters that determine the shape of the distribution. Using MINITAB, we will produce the probability distribution, and then graph it.

3. There is a difference between the theoretical probability distribution and the experimental probabilities derived from a random sample. Many times we use sample results to estimate the probability that an event will or will not occur. We can compare experimental to theoretical probabilities by taking some random samples and creating a relative frequency table. The relative frequencies are the estimates of the theoretical probabilities. Using MINITAB, we will create random samples and relative frequencies so that we can make the comparison between these experimental probabilities and the theoretical probabilities of the model.

The following are some examples that demonstrate how to use MINITAB to do the three things listed above.

A. Suppose you would like to look at a binomial probability table for n = 15 and p = .65. This table would show you all the possible outcomes of the random variable and their associated probabilities. You can produce a table in MINITAB as follows.

First, you must enter your X values in C1. These X values represent the number of successes in n trials. We know that the possible X values are 0,1,2,. . . n. In this case, n=15. A simple way to do this is to let MINITAB generate the numbers for you.

Click on:

CALC → MAKE PATTERNED DATA → SIMPLE SET OF NUMBERS

In the screen that appears, you want to:

> **Store patterned data in**: C1
> **From first value**: 0
> **To last value**: 15
> **In steps of**: 1

When these are filled in, click on **OK**. (Fig. 5-1). The numbers 0 through 15 should now be stored in C1.

· ·

Fig. 5-1

Simple Set of Numbers dialog box

$Store patterned data in:$ `c1`

From first value: `0`
To last value: `15`
In steps of: `1`

Number of times to list each value: `1`
Number of times to list the sequence: `1`

[Select] [Help] [OK] [Cancel]

B. Next, create the binomial probabilities. Click on:

CALC → PROBABILITY DISTRIBUTIONS → BINOMIAL.

On the screen that appears, select **PROBABILITY**. Then fill in the following:

Number of trials: 15
Probability of success: .65
Input column: C1
Optional storage: (leave blank)

When you click on **OK**, (Fig. 5-2), the probability distribution table will appear in the Session Window because you left **OPTIONAL STORAGE** blank. If you want to save the probabilities (as you will for a graph), you can fill in an **OPTIONAL STORAGE** column, such as C2. If you do this, the probabilities will now be stored in C2.

• •

Fig. 5-2

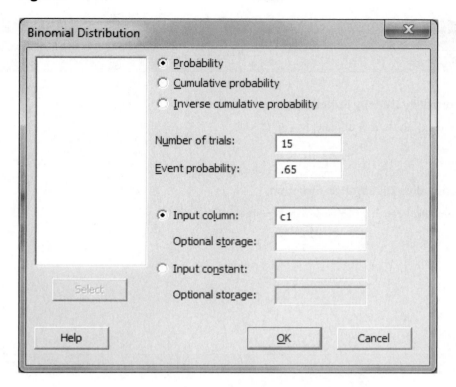

You may decide that rather than printing the entire probability table, you only want to find a specific probability. This is very simple to do. Use the same procedure as above, but this time leave **INPUT COLUMN** blank, and fill in **INPUT CONSTANT** with the desired X value. For example, to find P(X = 10), the **input constant** would be 10. Also, you will probably want to leave the **OPTIONAL STORAGE** blank so that the P(X=10) will be displayed in the Session Window. (When you try this, you should see P(X=10)=.2123) (Fig. 5-3)

You can also find the cumulative probability, which gives $P(X \le c)$ where c is a value you choose. To do this, simply click on **CUMULATIVE PROBABILITY** (instead of PROBABILITY) on the Binomial Input Screen. All the other options work exactly as explained above. For example, if your input constant is 5, then you will see in the Session Window $P(X \le 5) = .0124$. (Fig. 5-3)

• • • • • • • • • • • • • • • • • • • •

Fig. 5-3

You can also use the **CUMULATIVE PROBABILITY** to find P(X >c) by finding P(X ≤ c) and subtracting it from 1. For example, P(X > 5) = 1 - P(X ≤ 5) = 1 - .0124.

C. Now suppose you would like to graph a binomial probability distribution to see its shape. We will use a bar chart to graph a binomial distribution. You can practice using a binomial with n=10 and p=.7. You'll need to create and save the X values in C1 (X = 0,1,...,10) using:

CALC → MAKE PATTERNED DATA → SIMPLE SET OF NUMBERS

<u>and</u> the probability distribution in C2 using:

CALC → PROBABILITY DISTRIBUTIONS → BINOMIAL.

(Refer back to parts A and B on the previous pages for more detailed instructions on these steps.)

Be sure to use the **optional storage** in C2. (Fig. 5-4)

••••••••••••••••••••••

Fig. 5-4

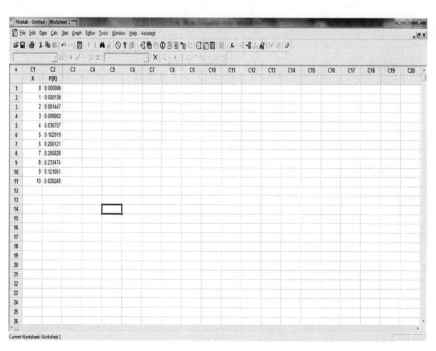

The Data Window should now have two columns filled. Name C1 "X",
and C2 "P(X)". (Fig. 5-5)

•••••••••••••••••••••

Fig. 5-5

Now to create a bar chart, click on: GRAPH → BAR CHART

On the pop-up screen, the **Bars represent: values from a table.** Select a **Simple** bar chart and click on OK. You will be at the main bar chart screen. The **Graph variable** is C2, where the probabilities are stored. The **Categorical variable** is C1, where the X values are stored. Be sure to click on the **Labels** button and add a **Title** to your graph which indicates which binomial distribution it is (i.e. Binomial n=10, p=.7), and a **Footnote** with your name and section number. Click on OK to view the bar chart. (Fig. 5-6)

• •
Fig. 5-6

Assignment

• •

Please answer all questions in the space provided. When you have completed this assignment, tear the pages along the perforation. Include with this assignment all computer work that is required to answer the questions. Each graph must be labeled with a title, axis labels, and a footnote with your name and section number. If the assignment requires you to print the Session Window, click in the Session Window and type your name and section number so you can identify your printout.

Begin with a clear worksheet.

1. In this problem, you will compare the theoretical probabilities to experimental probabilities that you obtain using relative frequencies from a random sample. You will use a coin flipping example since everyone is familiar with it. All of us know that the probability of a head is .5 when a fair coin is flipped. If you flip a coin 10 times, then this is a binomial experiment with n=10 and p=.5.

   a. First, create the theoretical probability distribution table, as explained above in parts A and B of the lesson. (Please note: In this example, n=10 and p=.5) Print this theoretical distribution in the Session Window (by leaving the **Optional Storage** field blank) so that you will have an output display of the theoretical probabilities for comparison purposes. In the display, notice that the theoretical probability of observing 3 heads in the 10 flips is 0.1172. Your experimental probability of 3 heads in 10 flips should be close to this.

   b. Next, you *could* run an experiment in which 200 people flip a coin 10 times each and record the number of heads they observe. You could then create a frequency table by counting up the number of people who flipped 0 Heads, 1 Head, 2 Heads, etc. If you then calculated the relative frequencies, you could compare them to the theoretical probabilities printed in your Session Window. Since finding 200 people who would be willing to flip a coin 10 times would be time consuming, you will let the computer simulate the experiment by generating 200 random samples of size 10, and storing the number of successes for each sample in one column. First, generate the 200 random samples of size 10.

   Click on: CALC → RANDOM DATA → BINOMIAL

Fill in the screen as follows:

Generate _200_ **Rows of Data**
Store in column(s): C3
Number of Trials: 10
Probability of Success: .5

Look at C3. Each of the 200 cells should contain a number between 0 and 10. This represents the number of Heads observed by each person. (Each cell represents a person.) Next, have MINITAB create the frequency table for you.

Click on: STAT → TABLES → TALLY INDIVIDUAL VARIABLES

Fill in the screen as follows:

Variables: C3
Select: **COUNTS** (an X should appear in the box)
Select: **PERCENTS** (an X should appear in the box)

A frequency table will appear in the Session Window. Look carefully at the table. Under the heading C3, you would like to see the numbers from 0 to 10. Because your data is random, it is possible that nobody observed 0 Heads or 10 Heads. In this case, the 0 and 10 will not appear under C3. Under the heading Count, you will see the frequencies. These represent the number of people (out of the 200 people) who tossed that number of Heads. Under the heading Percent, you will see the relative frequencies, as percentages. Compare these relative frequencies to the theoretical probabilities that you produced earlier in the Session Window. Since this is _random_ data, each student's frequency table will be a little different. In the chart below, fill in the theoretical and experimental probabilities using the computer output. Be sure to convert the relative frequency percentages to probabilities by moving the decimal point two places to the left so that you can make a direct comparison with the theoretical probabilities. (**Round all probabilities to 3 decimal places.**)

X	Theoretical Probability	Experimental Probability	Difference
0			
1			
2			
3	0.117		
4			
5			
6			
7			
8			
9			
10			

How close are the experimental probabilities to the theoretical probabilities? Write a brief comparison of the theoretical and experimental probabilities. For which X values are the probabilities very close? Where is the biggest difference? How could you change the experiment to improve these estimates?

2. It has been reported that 39% of college students graduate in 4 years. Consider a random sample of thirty students, and let the random variable X be the number who graduate in 4 years.

   a. Find the probability that exactly 13 students in the sample of 30 graduate in 4 years.

   b. Find the probability that 15 or fewer students in the sample graduate in 4 years. That is, find P(X ≤ 15).

   c. Using the results found in part b, calculate by hand the probability that more than 15 students in the sample graduate in 4 years.

3. According to the CDC, alcohol-impaired drivers are responsible for 32% of all car crash deaths in the US. Suppose we take a random sample of 100 car accident deaths and let X be the number that are alcohol related.

   a. Find the probability that fewer than 25 were alcohol related.

   b. Find the probability that between 23 and 40, inclusive, were alcohol related.

c. Find the probability that at least 38 were alcohol related.

4. The shape of the graph of a binomial distribution depends on the value of both n and p. To see how the shape changes for a fixed value of n, you will let p vary and graph each probability distribution. Let X be a binomial random variable with n=10.

   a. For p = .18, .47, and .88, obtain the binomial probability distribution and a bar chart of each distribution. Refer to part c of the lesson for instructions on graphing. (Be sure to hand the graphs in with your assignment.)

   b. For small values of p, the binomial distribution is skewed to the
   _____.

   For large values of p, the binomial distribution is skewed to the
   _____.

   For values of p near ____ the binomial distribution is nearly symmetric.

5. Now see what happens when you hold p constant and vary n. Let X be a binomial random variable with p=.24.

   a. Obtain the probability distribution and graph of the distribution for both n=10 and 30.

   b. Describe the shape of each graph. (Skewed right, skewed left, symmetric?)

   c. As n increases, the probability distribution becomes more
   _____ in shape.

Note: Be sure to print your graphs directly from Minitab or copy them to a Word document that you can print at the end of the assignment.

6. A Student Senate at a large university is made up of 60 students randomly selected to represent the entire student body. 20% of the students at this university are minorities. When the members of the senate are selected, only two members are minority

students. The Minority Caucus claims that this Senate is racially biased. They decide to use statistics to prove their claim.

a. Let X be the number of minority students who are selected for the senate.   Does this meet the criteria of a binomial experiment? _____

If so, what is n? _____

What is p? _____

b. Calculate the probability of the Senate being made up of so few minority students purely by chance. That is, find $P(X \leq 2)$ for this binomial problem.

c. Based on your answer to part b, would you be surprised if the senate had only 2 minority members? _____

Do you think the Minority Caucus is reasonable in their complaint of under-representation? _____
Explain.

d. Assuming that the senate represents the entire student body, how many minority students would you *expect* to be selected for the senate? Use the formula: $\mu = n*p$ to find the expected value: _____

e. Use your calculator to calculate the standard deviation of the number of minority students selected. Use the formula: $\sigma = $ sq.root($n*p*(1-p)$) to find the standard deviation: _____

f. Now suppose that the Student Senate has 9 minority students. Could the Minority Caucus make a case for racial bias in this case? Explain your answer using the Empirical Rule and the ($\mu \pm 2\sigma$) interval to find what a typical outcome would be.

Note: Print your Session Window with your binomial probabilities.

Chapter 6

The Normal Random Variable

A normal random variable is one that follows a bell-shaped probability distribution. In class, you may have learned to calculate a normal probability by first standardizing and then looking up the Z in the standard normal table in your textbook. In this lab, you will be doing normal probability problems, but you will be using MINITAB to calculate the probabilities. MINITAB calculates the probabilities directly, so there is no need to standardize or to use the standard normal table.

In this lab, you will solve two types of problems using the normal random variable. You will also plot normal distributions with different means and standard deviations.

Normal Probability Problems:

For the first type of problem, you will be given the mean and standard deviation for a <u>normal</u> random variable, X. You will then be asked to calculate probabilities such as $P(X \leq a)$, $P(X \geq b)$ or $P(a \leq X \leq b)$ where a and b are given.

For example, if X is a normal random variable with $\mu = 100$ and $\sigma = 20$, what is the probability that an observed value of X will be less than 90?

To do this in MINITAB, click on:

CALC $\rightarrow$ PROBABILITY DISTRIBUTIONS $\rightarrow$ NORMAL

In the next window, select **CUMULATIVE PROBABILITY**. (Cumulative probability 'accumulates' <u>all</u> probability to the left of the input constant.) Enter the values for the mean and standard deviation. In this example, the **mean** is 100 and the **standard deviation** is 20. Next select **INPUT CONSTANT** by highlighting the circle to the left and then enter the value 90 in the box to the right of **INPUT CONSTANT**. Click on **OK**. (Fig. 6-1)

• •
Fig. 6-1

The results should appear in your Session Window. Under the column headed P(X ≤ x) you should see 0.3085. This is the probability that the random variable, X, takes on values less than or equal to 90. Thus,   P(X ≤ 90) = .308538. (Fig. 6-2)

• •

Fig. 6-2

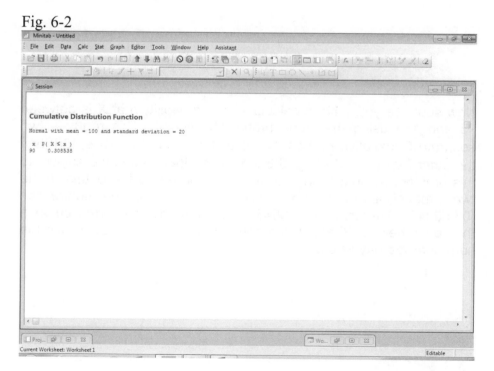

In the space below, draw a normal curve by hand and shade in the area you wanted to calculate and label the area with the appropriate value. In this example, the label should be the value 0.3085 (rounded to the nearest thousandth).

Now suppose you wish to calculate $P(X \geq 130)$ using the same normal probability model with $\mu = 100$ and $\sigma = 20$. Use the same set of commands:

CALC $\rightarrow$ PROBABILITY DISTRIBUTIONS $\rightarrow$ NORMAL

This time, the **INPUT CONSTANT** is 130 (instead of 90). Notice your results give $P(X \leq 130) = .933193$ since cumulative probability always gives you the area <u>less</u> than the value entered (Fig. 6-3). Since you want the $P(X \geq 130)$, the answer you want is the complement of what MINITAB calculated. So, take the MINITAB result for this example and subtract it from 1 to get your answer. In the space below draw a normal curve and shade in the area you are interested in finding. You should label the area on the graph appropriately. (The answer is 1 - 0.933193 = 0.066807)

Now suppose you wish to calculate the probability that X is between 95 and 135 using the same probability model. This requires two separate Cumulative Probability calculations: one for $P(X \leq 135)$ and the other for $P(X \leq 95)$ (Fig. 6-3). You can then obtain the answer to this problem by subtracting the two probabilities. After obtaining the two probabilities from the Session Window, do the subtraction (0.959941 - 0.401294 = 0.558647), and then draw the normal curve in the space below. Shade in the appropriate area and label it with the correct probability value.

• •
Fig. 6-3

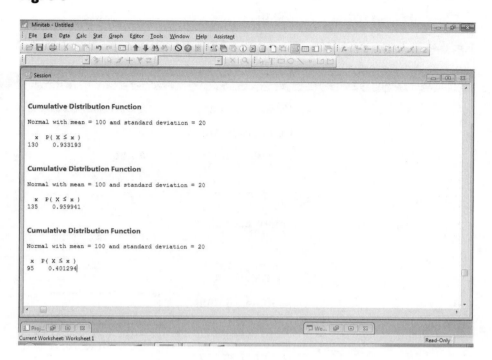

Inverse Normal Probability Problems:
• •

The second type of problem is called an Inverse Normal Problem. In this type of problem you are given that X is a Normal random variable with a specific mean and standard deviation. Then, you are asked to find the value, k, that is the cut-off point for a given percentage of the values of the random variable X.

For example, suppose X is a normal random variable with $\mu = 100$ and $\sigma = 20$. What value of X marks the lower 20% of the distribution? (Thus, find the 20th percentile.)

To do this, the MINITAB commands are:

CALC $\rightarrow$ PROBABILITY DISTRIBUTION $\rightarrow$ NORMAL

In the next window, select **INVERSE CUMULATIVE PROBABILITY**. Enter the values of the mean and standard deviation. For this type of problem, the **INPUT CONSTANT** will be the area, a decimal number between 0 and 1. In the example we are using, the **INPUT**

CONSTANT is .20. (Since 20% of the area is to the left of the value we are looking for.) Click on **OK**. (Fig. 6-4)

• •

Fig. 6-4 .

The answer appears in the Session Window under the column labeled 'X'. For this example, the answer is 83.1676 (Fig 6-5). This means that for the normal probability distribution with μ = 100 and σ = 20, 20% of the data lies below the value 83.1676. Draw the normal curve, shade in the lower 20% and mark the value 83.1676 under the curve.

• •

Fig. 6-5

Consider the following problem: If X is a normal random variable with μ = 100 and σ = 20, what is the X-value that will mark off the upper 20% of the probability? Since MINITAB always calculates P(X ≤ some value), you must ask for an Inverse Cumulative Probability of 80%, since the point that marks the top 20% is the same point that marks the lower 80%. So, follow the same steps as in the previous example and simply change the **INPUT CONSTANT** to .80. In the Session Window, your answer should be 116.8324. Draw the curve and label it appropriately.

The last type of problem is the following. Suppose X is a Normal random variable with μ = 100 and σ = 20. What values of X mark off the central 80% of the distribution? If you mark off the central 80%, the remaining 20% will be divided evenly into 10% in each tail of the distribution. Thus, in the lower tail there is 10% below the value and in the upper tail there is 10% above the value. You need to calculate two **INVERSE CUMULATIVE PROBABILITIES**. For the lower tail, use an **INPUT CONSTANT** of .10 and for the upper tail, use an **INPUT CONSTANT** of .90. (Recall, the top 10% point is the same as the lower 90% point). Your two X-values are 74.3690 and 125.6310.

This means that 80% of the data lies between these two values. Draw the curve and label it appropriately.

Graphing a Normal Curve:

To graph a normal curve by hand is a simple task, and yet it takes a little thought to really understand the difference between two normal distributions. You know that the normal distribution is centered around its mean, and that most of its area falls within three standard deviations of the mean. MINITAB can draw a normal distribution quite easily, and can demonstrate the difference between two normal distributions. For example, suppose we want to compare a normal distribution with $\mu = 50$ and $\sigma = 5$ to a normal distribution with $\mu = 40$ and $\sigma = 5$. To do this in MINITAB, you first have to store some X values in C1 and the corresponding probabilities in C2. Since most all of the probability falls within 3σ of μ, our first distribution should fall within the interval $50 \pm 3(5)$, which is 35 to 65. Our second should fall within the interval $40 \pm 3(5)$, which is 25 to 55. To do this in MINITAB, we will first store X values for each distribution. We will put X values between 35 and 65 in C1, and X values between 25 and 55 in C3. After this is done, we will store normal probabilities for each distribution in C2 and C4. Lastly, we will plot the two distributions on the same graph.

Click on: CALC → MAKE PATTERNED DATA → SIMPLE SET OF NUMBERS

Fill in: **Store Patterned Data In**: C1
             From first value: 35
             To last value: 65
             In steps of: 1   (Fig. 6-6)

The above information is for the first distribution. Repeat the process for the second distribution, but store the data in C3. Use 25 as the first value and 55 as the last value.

• •

Fig. 6-6

Simple Set of Numbers

| Store patterned data in: | c1 |

From first value: 35

To last value: 65

In steps of: 1

List each value 1 times

List the whole sequence 1 times

Select

Help | OK | Cancel

Next store the probabilities.

CALC → PROBABILITY DISTRIBUTION → NORMAL

Fill in:

> **Probability Density**   (Be sure to select Probability Density)
> **Mean**: 50
> **Standard Deviation**: 5
> **Input Column**: C1
> **Optional Storage**: C2 (Fig. 6-7)

Repeat the process for the second distribution. This time $\mu=40$ and $\sigma=5$. The Input Column is C3 and the Optional Storage is C4.

• •

Fig. 6-7

Now do the graphing. We will graph both normal curves on the same page so that we can compare the two distributions.

Click on: GRAPH → SCATTERPLOT

On the pop-up screen, select the plot icon **With Connect and Groups** and click OK to view the main plot window. In the input screen, the **Y variables** are the probabilities contained in C2 and C4. The **X variables** are the X-values contained in C1 and C3. Click on the check box to select **X-Y pairs form groups.** (Fig. 6-8)

• •

Fig. 6-8

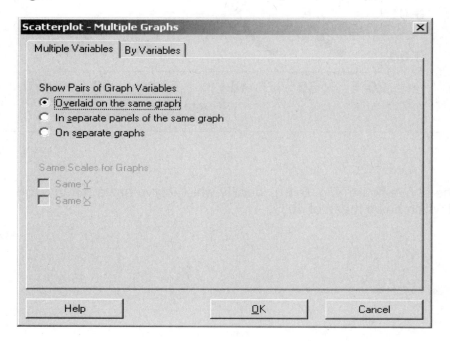

To graph the two curves on one page, click on the **Multiple Graphs** button. Select **Overlaid on the same graph.**   Click on OK. (Fig. 6-9)

• •

Fig. 6-9

Click on **OK** again and you should see the graphs (Fig. 6-10). Notice that they look identical, except that one is shifted over. This is because the two distributions have different means, but the same standard deviations. In the assignment below, you will explore what happens when the means are the same, but the standard deviations are different.

• •

Fig. 6-10

In the above figure (Fig. 6-10), identify which curve has a mean of 50 and which has a mean of 40.

Assignment

Please answer all questions in the space provided. When you have completed this assignment, tear the pages along the perforation. Include with this assignment all computer work that is required to answer the questions. Each graph must be labeled with a title, axis labels, and a footnote with your name and section number. If the assignment requires you to print the Session Window, click in the Session Window and type your name and section number so that you can identify your printout.

In the space provided for each question, draw the proper normal curve and label the curve appropriately. Be sure to shade the area described in the problem, identify and label the mean, and label the X-values associated with the shaded areas. Please show all your work and circle your final answer to each problem. Also, label each section of the output with the correct problem number.

1. If X is normal with $\mu = 100$ and $\sigma = 10$, what is the probability that X exceeds 115?

$\mu = 100$
$\sigma = 10$
$P(x \geq 115)$
$P(x \leq 115)$

Answer
$1 - .933193 = .066807$

$= 1 - P(x \leq 115)$

2. If X is normal with $\mu = 100$ and $\sigma = 10$, find the 90th percentile of this distribution.

.90

86 90 100 110 120

?

ANSWER = 112.816

3. If X is normal with $\mu = 200$ and $\sigma = 10$, what is the probability that X will be between 188 and 206? $P(188 \leq X \leq 206) = .725747 - .115070 =$

$.610677$

188 200 206

$P(X \leq 206) = .725747$

$(X \leq 188) = .115070$

4. If X is normal with μ = 8.48 and σ = 1.60, find the probability that X exceeds 6.96? $P(X > 6.96)$

$1 - .171056 = .828944$

$P(x \le 6.96) = .171056$

5. If X is normal with μ = 8.48 and σ = 1.60, what are the two values of X which include the central 80% of the probability?

$.80$

8.48

$P(x \le ?) = .10$ $P(x \le ?) = .90$

$? = 6.42952$ $? = 10.5305$

6. If Z is standard normal, above what value of z is 1% of the probability?
    (Recall that μ = 0 and σ = 1 for the standard normal).

$.01$

10%

0

$? $

$.99$

$? = 2.32635$

7. If X is normal with μ = 200 and σ = 11, between what two values of X is the central 50% of the probability?

$P(A \le X \le B) = .5$

$.5$

$B = 207.419$

$A = 192.581$

$.25 A$ 200 B

$.75$

8. If SAT scores are normal with μ = 500 and σ = 50, what is the probability that a randomly selected person will have an SAT score higher than 680?

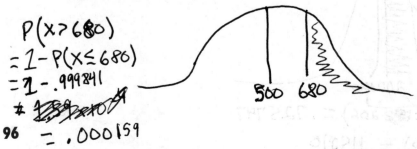

$P(X > 680)$

$= 1 - P(X \le 680)$

$= 1 - .999841$

$\#$

$= .000159$

9. The MATH SAT Scores for all students who applied to the School of Engineering are normally distributed with μ =629 and σ = 60. The School of Engineering has decided to accept those students whose scores fall within the top 15%. What is the minimum score an applicant must have in order to be accepted into the Engineering School?

Rounded to 692

10. The average length of time required for students to complete a test in an Introductory Statistics course is found to be 50 minutes with a standard deviation of 12 minutes. If students are allowed 80 minutes to complete the test, approximately what percentage of the students will have sufficient time to complete the test? (Assume that the time required to complete the test follows a normal distribution.)

$P(x \leq 80) = .993790$

11. The daily sales at the campus bookstore throughout the school year have a probability distribution that is approximately normal with μ = $1530 and σ = $120. The bookstore must have at least $1200 in sales per day to break even. What is the probability that on a given day the bookstore will not break even?

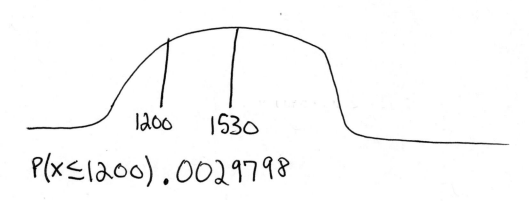

$P(x \leq 1200) .0029798$

12. Use a graph to see the effect of changing the standard deviation of a normal distribution. (Follow the graphing instructions in the Graphing a Normal Curve section of the lesson.) Let $\mu = 100$ for both distributions, but let $\sigma = 10$ for one and $\sigma = 20$ for the other distribution. Recall, that for each distribution the first X value should be 3σ below the mean of 100, and the last X value should be 3σ above the mean of 100. For both distributions, when you instruct MINITAB to create the X values for you, this time set the data **IN STEPS OF** 2. Graph both distributions on the same page.

a. Explain what changing the standard deviation from 10 to 20 does to the shape of the distribution.

$$\mu \pm 3\sigma$$

$$100 \pm 3(10) \qquad 100 \pm 3(20)$$
$$(70, 130) \qquad (40, 160)$$

Chapter 7

The Central Limit Theorem and the Sampling Distribution of the Sample Mean

In Chapter 6, we studied the normal probability distribution for a random variable, X. Based on this distribution, we can calculate probabilities for specific values of the random variable. For example, it is known that IQ's are normally distributed with $\mu = 100$ and $\sigma = 15$. Suppose we want to calculate the probability that a randomly selected individual has an IQ greater than 130. That is, we wish to calculate $P(X > 130)$. This is easily done using MINITAB's normal probability distribution, as explained in Chapter 6.

In this chapter, rather than looking at one person's IQ, we will consider the *average* IQ for a sample of n individuals. Suppose we want to calculate $P(\bar{X} > 130)$ for a sample of n = 35 individuals. This is an entirely different question from the one above because now we are asking to calculate the probability that the *average* IQ for the group is greater than 130. What we are now asking is a probability question about $\bar{X}$, instead of X, so we need to study the behavior of $\bar{X}$. Since $\bar{X}$ is calculated from a **sample** of x's, the probability distribution of $\bar{X}$ is called a **Sampling Distribution**.

The Central Limit Theorem:

You will discover in this lesson that the mean of the sampling distribution of $\bar{X}$, $(\mu_{\bar{x}})$, is equal to the mean of the original population μ. The standard deviation of the sampling distribution of $\bar{X}$, $(\sigma_{\bar{x}})$, is approximately equal to the population standard deviation divided by the square root of n, $\sigma / \sqrt{n}$). For "large" samples n > 30), the sampling distribution of $\bar{X}$ is approximately normally distributed, regardless of the shape of the underlying population. This is the Central Limit Theorem, which you have probably studied in class by now.

In order to study the behavior of $\bar{X}$, we will create several sampling distributions in the following way:

1. Start with a population of x's.

2. From that population take a random sample of size n.

3. Calculate the mean, $\bar{x}$, of that sample.

4. Repeat this process that is, take another random sample of size n and calculate the mean of this sample).

5. Repeat this process indefinitely and you would generate a population of means, $\bar{x}$'s. This is called the Sampling Distribution of the Sample Mean. Note: in this lab you will create a "pseudo-population" by repeating the process a fixed number of times, rather than an indefinite number of times.)

The questions that we want to answer are the following:

a. How does the mean of the sampling distribution $\mu_{\bar{x}}$ compare to the mean of the original population, μ)?

b. How does the standard deviation of the sampling distribution $\sigma_{\bar{x}}$), compare to the standard deviation of the original population, σ)?

c. How does the shape of the sampling distribution compare to the shape of the original population?

Applications of the Central Limit Theorem:

Let's return to the example concerning the average IQ of a sample of 35 individuals. We know that IQ's are normally distributed with mean =100 and standard deviation =15. The Central Limit Theorem tells us that for n=35 the Sampling Distribution of $\bar{X}$ is normally distributed with $\mu_{\bar{x}} = 100$ and $\sigma_{\bar{x}} = \sigma / \sqrt{n} = 15/\sqrt{35} = 2.54$. Now suppose we are interested in calculating the probability that the average IQ for our group is greater than 105.

We can use MINITAB to calculate $P\bar{X} > 105$). To do this, we will use the same procedure that we used in Chapter 6 for Normal Probability Problems. However, since we are asking a probability question about $\bar{X}$, we must use the standard deviation of the sampling distribution of $\bar{X}$. This can be pre-calculated using either your hand calculator or MINITAB's calculator.

Now, let's calculate $P(\bar{X} > 105)$ for our sample of n=35 using MINITAB. To do this, click on:

CALC → PROBABILITY DISTRIBUTIONS → NORMAL

In the next window, select **CUMULATIVE PROBABILITY.** In this example, the **mean** is 100 and the **standard deviation** is 2.54 which is 15/$\sqrt{35}$). Next select **INPUT CONSTANT** and enter the value 105. Click on **OK** and the result that appears in the Session Window is P($\overline{X} \leq 105$) which is .9755. Since we are interested in P($\overline{X} > 105$), we must subtract .9755 from 1.

Assignment

• •

Please answer all questions in the space provided. When you have completed this assignment, tear the pages along the perforation. Include with this assignment all computer work that is required to answer the questions. Each graph must be labeled with a title, axis labels, and a footnote with your name and section number. If the assignment requires you to print the Session Window, click in the Session Window and type your name and section number so you can identify your printout.

In this assignment, in order to study the behavior of $\bar{X}$, you will be generating random samples. Because the samples are random, each individual's samples will be different.

1. Begin with a population that is NORMAL with a mean of 100 and a standard deviation of 10. Take 300 random samples of size n=2.

   To do this, click on: CALC → RANDOM DATA → NORMAL

   On the input screen that appears, **Generate** 300 **rows of data**, **store in** C1 and C2. Be sure to enter the **mean** = 100 and **standard deviation** = 10. After you click on **OK**, you should see data in the Data Window in C1 and C2. Each **row** represents a random sample of n=2 data points from the population.

   Now use ROW STATISTICS to calculate the mean for each sample of n=2.

   To do this, click on: CALC → ROW STATISTICS.

   On the input screen that appears, select **MEAN**. Use C1-C2 as the **input variables** and **store result in** C3.

   Now look at the different columns. Name C3 so that when you graph the histograms, you will be able to identify the sampling distribution easily. To do this, click on the Data Window to move the cursor down to it. In the gray cell at the top of C3, type in "Norn=2)" to identify the distribution and sample size. Each entry in C3 should be the average of the values in C1 and C2. Use your calculator to verify this by choosing any row and averaging the values in C1 and C2 and confirm that this is the corresponding value in C3. <u>Show your calculation below.</u>

What you have created in C3 approximately represents a Sampling Distribution of $\bar{X}$. Find the mean and standard deviation of the Sampling Distribution. To do this, click on:

STAT → BASIC STATISTICS → DISPLAY DESCRIPTIVE STATISTICS

On the input screen that appears, select C3 for the **Variable.** The results will be in the Session Window. **Wait until after problem 5 to print the Session Window.)**

a. How does the mean of C3 ($\mu_{\bar{x}}$) compare to the mean of the original population, μ? Recall that the mean of the original population is 100. Note: $\mu_{\bar{x}}$ should be approximately equal to μ).

  $\mu_{\bar{x}} =$ _____

Are the two values close? _____ If so, the results of your simulation of a sampling distribution confirm that: $\mu_{\bar{x}}$ should be approximately equal to μ.

b. How does $\sigma_{\bar{x}}$, the standard deviation of C3, compare to the standard deviation of the original population, σ? Note: $\sigma_{\bar{x}}$ should be approx. equal to $\sigma / \sqrt{n}$). For this example, n = 2 and σ = 10.

  Using your calculator, calculate $\sigma / \sqrt{n}$. _____

  Compare your calculation to the standard deviation of C3.
  _____

  Are the two numbers close? _____ If so, the results of your simulation of a sampling distribution confirm that $\sigma_{\bar{x}}$ should be approx. equal to $\sigma / \sqrt{n}$.

c. Now compare the shape of a set of data from the original population, C1, with the shape of the sampling distribution, C3. First, in the Worksheet, give C1 the name: "Population Data". Give C3 the name: "Sample Means n=2)". Next, click on: GRAPH → HISTOGRAM. Click on the SIMPLE histogram icon.

Select both C1 and C3 for the GRAPH VARIABLES. If you then click on the button labeled MULTIPLE GRAPHS, you can select **SAME Y** and also **SAME X, including bins** by clicking on the check boxes. Now both histograms will have the same scale. Put a title on the graphs. The title should identify the population distribution: "Underlying Population: Normal". **Do Not** use Axis Labels here. Let MINITAB use the column name so that you can tell which column of data the histogram is displaying. Print the two histograms or copy them to a Word document and print the document at the end of this assignment. In the space below write a summary of the similarities and differences between the shapes of the two columns. Be specific. Comment on which histograms look normal. Compare the centers and spreads of the two graphs.

2. Next begin with a population that is not normal. A UNIFORM distribution has a flat shape with data that is evenly distributed. It looks like a rectangle. We will use a UNIFORM distribution with endpoints 70 and 130. This distribution has a mean, μ), equal to 100 and a standard deviation, σ), equal to 17.3. Fig. 7-1)

● ●

Fig. 7-1

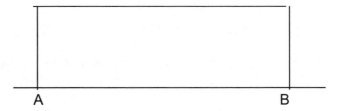

The values of A and B represent the endpoints of the distribution. In our example, A will be 70 and B will be 130.

To start with a clear Data Window, highlight and delete all data cells. This should give you a blank Data Window, but the Session Window should still have the **Descriptive Statistics** from the last example. Take 300 random samples of size n=2 from a UNIFORM distribution on the interval 70 to 130. Use the commands described above in problem 1, except this time select **UNIFORM** distribution with **lower endpoint** 70 and **upper endpoint** 130. Use **ROW STATISTICS** to calculate the mean for each sample of n=2 and **store results in** C3. Name C3 appropriately, i.e. "Unin=2)".

Each entry in C3 should be the average of the values in C1 and C2. Verify this by choosing any row and averaging the values in C1 and C2 and confirm that this is the corresponding value in C3. Show this work below.

 What you have created in C3 is a representation of the Sampling Distribution of $\bar{X}$.

   a. Use **DISPLAY DESCRIPTIVE STATISTICS** for C3 to find the mean and standard deviation of the values in C3.

       How does the mean of C3 compare to the mean of the original population? The mean of the original population is 100).

       $\mu_{\bar{x}} =$ _____

       Are the two values close? _____ If so, the results of your simulation of a sampling distribution confirm that $\mu_{\bar{x}}$ should be approximately equal to μ.

   b. How does $\sigma_{\bar{x}}$, the standard deviation of C3, compare to the standard deviation of the original population, σ? Note: $\sigma_{\bar{x}}$ should be approx. equal to $\sigma / \sqrt{n}$). For this example, n = 2 and σ = 17.3.

       Using your calculator, calculate $\sigma / \sqrt{n}$. _____

       Compare your calculation to the standard deviation of C3. _____

       Are the two numbers close? _____ If so, the results of your simulation of a sampling distribution confirm that $\sigma_{\bar{x}}$ should be approx. equal to $\sigma / \sqrt{n}$.

   c. Now compare the shape of data from the original population in C1 with the shape of the sampling distribution in C3. C3. First, in the Worksheet, give C1 the name: "Population Data". Give C3 the name: "Sample Means n=2)". Use the same procedure for making histograms as was described above in problem 1. Use C1 and C3 for the histograms. Put a title on the graphs. The title should identify the population distribution: "Underlying Population: Uniform". Print the two histograms or copy them to a Word document and print the document at the end of this assignment. In the space below write a summary of the similarities and differences between the shapes of the two columns.

Be specific. Be sure to comment on shape, center, and variation for each histogram.

3. Continue this example with the Uniform distribution, but increase the sample size from n=2 to n=30. Again, start with a clear worksheet. This time you need to **generate** 300 **rows of data** and **store in** C1-C30. Now each row represents a sample of n=30 data points from the population. Use **ROW STATISTICS** to calculate the **mean** for each sample of n=30. The **input variables** should be C1-C30, and you can **store result in** C31. Name C31 "Unin=30)". Each entry in C31 should be the average of the values in C1 through C30. What you have created in C31 is a representation of the Sampling Distribution of $\bar{x}$.

a. Use the **DISPLAY DESCRIPTIVE STATISTICS** on C31 to find the mean and standard deviation of the values in C31.

How does the mean of C31 compare to the mean of the original population? The mean of original population is 100).

$\mu_{\bar{x}} =$ _____

Are the two values close? _____ If so, the results of your simulation of a sampling distribution confirm that $\mu_{\bar{x}}$ should be approximately equal to μ.

b. How does $\sigma_{\bar{x}}$, the standard deviation of C31, compare to the standard deviation of the original population, σ? Note: $\sigma_{\bar{x}}$ should be approx. equal to $\sigma/\sqrt{n}$). For this example, n = 30 and σ = 17.3.

Using your calculator, calculate $\sigma/\sqrt{n}$. _____

Compare your calculation to the standard deviation of C31.

_____

Are the two numbers close? _____ If so, the results of your simulation of a sampling distribution confirm that $\sigma_{\bar{x}}$ should be approx. equal to $\sigma / \sqrt{n}$.

c. Now compare the shape of data from the original population in C1 with the shape of the sampling distribution in C31. First, in the Worksheet, give C1 the name: "Population Data". Give C31 the name: "Sample Means n=30)". Use the same procedure for making histograms as was described above in problem 1. Use C1 and C31 for the histograms. Put a title on the graphs. The title should identify the population distribution: "Underlying Population: Uniform". Print the two histograms or copy them to a Word document and print the document at the end of this assignment. In the space below write a summary of the similarities and differences between the shapes of the two columns. Be specific. Be sure to comment on shape, center, and variation for each histogram. Be specific.

4. The daily sales at the campus bookstore throughout the school year have a probability distribution that is approximately normal with mean = \$1530 and standard deviation = \$120. The bookstore must have a monthly **average** of at least \$1500 to break even. Assuming a month has 30 days, what is the probability that, for a given month, the bookstore breaks even? That is, find $P\bar{x} > 1500$).

$\mu_{\bar{x}}$ = _____

$\sigma_{\bar{x}}$= _____

$P(\bar{X} \leq 1500)$ = _____

$P(\bar{X} > 1500)$ = _____

So the probability that the bookstore breaks even in a given month is _____ .

5. On a particular stretch of highway, the State Police know that the average speed is 62 mph with a standard deviation of 5 mph. On a busy holiday weekend, the police are concerned that people travel too fast. So they randomly monitor speeds of a sample of 50 cars and record an average speed of 66 mph. Find the probability of obtaining a **sample average speed** of 66 mph or more if, in fact, the true average speed for all cars on that holiday weekend is still 62 mph?

$\mu_{\bar{x}}$ = _____

$\sigma_{\bar{x}}$ = _____

$P(\bar{x} \le 66)$ = _____

$P(\bar{x} \ge 66)$ = _____

The probability that the average speed of the sample is 66 mph or greater, assuming that the average speed of all cars is 62 mph is _____.

So, is it very unlikely to get a sample average of 66 mph or more if, in fact, the true population average is 62 mph?

Based on this probability, are the police justified in their concern? Explain your answer.

Chapter 8

Confidence Interval Estimation

One of the very important statistical inference problems is estimation. Estimation is concerned with finding the value of a population parameter (for example, μ, the population mean), without actually obtaining the data from the entire population. Instead of working with an entire population you can simply take a random sample from the population and use the sample information to provide an estimate of the population parameter.

There are two types of estimation methods: point estimation and interval estimation. For example, you can calculate the mean of a sample and use this to estimate the mean of the population from which the sample was taken. In this case, the sample mean, $\overline{x}$, is a *point estimate* of the population mean, μ. Alternatively, you can use the sample mean as a starting point and add a margin of error, creating an *interval estimate* of μ.

Any sample is usually only a small part of the population, so it is very unlikely that the sample mean will be *exactly* equal to the population mean, but we hope it will be close. Since μ is unknown, there is no way to know how close $\overline{x}$, the point estimate, is to μ. Because of this uncertainty, point estimates are used less frequently than interval estimates.

An interval estimate uses a range of values to estimate μ. To create the interval, start with the sample mean, $\overline{x}$, since it is our "best guess" of the value of μ. Now add and subtract a margin of error. The margin of error depends upon the standard deviation of the sampling distribution of $\overline{x}$ and the "confidence coefficient".

Before we look at any intervals, let's discuss the confidence coefficient. It measures the confidence we have in the process we are using to construct the interval, which is called a *confidence interval*. For example, if you choose a 95% confidence coefficient and you construct hundreds of confidence intervals, then approximately 95% of these intervals will include μ, the true population mean and 5% of them will fail to include μ. These intervals that fail to include μ are usually the result of obtaining a random sample in which $\overline{x}$ is very different from μ. Of course, since μ is unknown, you cannot determine which of the intervals DO contain μ and which intervals DO NOT contain μ. However, you "have confidence" that the process you used will result in an interval that contains μ, the true mean of the populations, 95% of the time.

Confidence Interval Formulas:

• •

There are two basic confidence interval formulas for μ, the Z-Interval and the t-Interval.

The Z - confidence interval for μ is:

$$\bar{x} \pm z^* \sigma / \sqrt{n}$$

This formula is used when the population is normally distributed and σ is known. The z value in the formula comes from the standard normal table and is based on the confidence coefficient (typically 90%, 95%, 99%).

The t- confidence interval for μ is:

$$\bar{x} \pm t^* s / \sqrt{n}$$

This formula is used when the population is normally distributed and σ is unknown. The t value in the formula comes from the t-table and is based on the confidence coefficient.

If you look at the two formulas, you will notice that they are very similar. Both formulas start with $\bar{x}$, a point estimate of μ, and add and subtract a margin of error. The margin of error is composed of a table value (Z or t), a standard deviation (σ or s), and a sample size. Both formulas apply to normally distributed data. In fact, that restriction can be relaxed as n (the sample size) increases. It is only when n is small (approximately 20 or less) that normality is critical. Regardless of sample size, it is always a good idea to plot the data and look for outliers (unusual data points) and for skewness in the data. But, these concerns are more serious in small samples.

In practice, σ, the population standard deviation, is rarely known, so the Z-interval is not used very often. Note: Some textbooks recommend the use of the Z-interval for large samples (n > 30), even when σ is unknown. In these cases, s, the sample standard deviation, is a good approximation for σ and is used in place of σ in the formula. For large samples, the Z-interval and t-interval will yield almost identical results.

Example 1:

In this example, you will study the process of constructing confidence intervals. You will begin with a normally distributed population with a <u>known</u> mean equal to 69 and a <u>known</u> standard deviation equal to 3. From this population, select 50 random samples of size n=30. To do this, click on:

CALC → RANDOM DATA → NORMAL

In the screen that appears, you want to:

Generate: 30 rows   (since n=30)
Store in: C1 – C50   (since we want 50 samples)
Mean: 69
Standard Deviation: 3

Each of the 50 columns is a random sample of size n=30 from the normal population with μ=69 and σ=3. Now use the 50 columns of data to construct 50 different 95% confidence intervals for μ. Each confidence interval is an interval estimate of μ. In this example, we already know that μ is equal to 69, so we can actually see how well the confidence intervals do at estimating μ. Since σ is known, use the 1-Sample-Z.

To construct the intervals, click on:

STAT → BASIC STATISTICS → 1-SAMPLE-Z

In the screen that appears, you will use each of the 50 columns to construct 50 different confidence intervals. The first input box on this screen should read "**one or more samples, each in a column.**" In the second input box, type in C1-C50. Enter the population standard deviation, 3. Click on **Options** and enter 95 for the **Confidence Interval.** Make sure that the Alternative hypothesis box reads "**mean ≠ hypothesized mean.**" Click on **Ok** twice. The confidence intervals will appear in the Session Window. **Maximize** the Session Window to easily view the confidence intervals. (Fig. 8-1).

Note: Your intervals will be different since this is RANDOM data.

• •
Fig. 8-I

Each row contains information about one of your samples of data. For example, the first row shows N, MEAN, STDEV, SE MEAN and 95% CI for the first set of 30 data points that you randomly generated in C1. The 95% confidence interval for the first sample is (68.0487, 70.1957). Recall that μ is 69 in this population. So this particular confidence interval DID accurately estimate μ since 69 lies between the lower limit of the confidence interval (68.0487) and the upper limit (70.1957). Now notice the confidence interval that was created from the data in C7: (69.0136, 71.1606). This interval failed to correctly estimate μ since 69 is not contained in the interval.

Look at all 50 intervals. Notice that only 1 interval (C7) does not contain μ. So this process of estimating μ worked for 49 out of 50 samples, or approximately 98% of the time. This percentage is very close to our chosen confidence level of 95%.

In this example, μ was known. Because we knew μ, we were able to determine which confidence intervals contained μ and which did not. In practice, a confidence interval is used to estimate an unknown μ and therefore, we would not know which intervals correctly estimated μ. What you saw above was that the process works approximately 95% of the time. (Recall that the confidence coefficient we are using in this example is 95%.)

Example 2:

For this example, you will enter the data directly into C1 in the Data Window. Start by closing the current worksheet. You will now see a new worksheet window in which you can enter the data.

Here is a random sample of final exam scores for 20 randomly selected students in a large Introductory Statistics class.

88 67 73 65 89 77 81 94 99 54 65 56 79 88 72 64 55 69 71 55

You are interested in constructing a confidence interval for μ, the average exam grade for all students in the course.

Since this is a small dataset it is critical that the assumption of normality is satisfied. So we will begin with a graph that will look for normality (or lack of normality).

Click on: GRAPH $\rightarrow$ PROBABILITY PLOTS and select Single. On the screen that appears, select C1 as your **Graph Variable.** Click on **OK**, and a Normal Probability Plot of the data will appear. This plot is used to test the normality or lack of normality of a dataset. The graph shows the data points with a line drawn through the points and with confidence bands on either side of the line. If the data points are fairly linear and mostly contained within the confidence bands, then we can safely conclude that the data is from a normal population. In other words, there is no indication of lack of normality. Note: We will look at this graph and its output in more detail when we study Hypothesis Testing in the next chapter. (Fig. 8-2)

Fig. 8-2

Our graph shows that there is some scatter of the points around the line but that the data generally falls in a linear pattern and all the points fall inside the confidence bands. We can assume that our underlying population is normal.

Now, you are ready to proceed with the t-interval.

Click on: STAT → BASIC STATISTICS → 1-SAMPLE t. The first input box on this screen should read "**one or more samples, each in a column**." In the second input box, select C1. Click on **Options** and enter 95 for the **Confidence Interval.** Make sure that the Alternative hypothesis box reads "**mean ≠ hypothesized mean**." Click on **Ok.**

Click on: **Graphs** and select Histogram and Boxplot.

The graphs will be displayed and the Confidence interval will appear in the Session Window. (Fig. 8-3).

Fig. 8-3

These graphs give additional pictures of our dataset. The boxplot shows some right-skewness in our sample data but no outliers. The histogram also shows the right-skewness of the data. Both graphs also display the confidence interval for μ as a line drawn below the graph itself.

With small datasets it is difficult to use the shape of the histogram to determine the shape of the underlying population. As you can see, this histogram clearly does not look very normal. That is why we rely on the Normal Probability Plot to determine normality of the underlying population rather than simply looking at the histogram of the sample data.

The Session Window contains descriptive statistics for the sample and a 95% Confidence Interval for μ. The Confidence Interval states that the average score on the exam was between 66.70 and 79.40.

Assignment

· ·

Please answer all questions in the space provided. When you have completed this assignment, tear the pages along the perforation. Include with this assignment all computer work that is required to answer the questions. Each graph must be labeled with a title, axis labels, and a footnote with your name and section number. If the assignment requires you to print the Session Window, click in the Session Window and type your name and section number so you can identify your printout.

1. Using the procedure explained in Example 1 generate 50 random samples of size n=30 from a normal population with μ=69 and σ=3.

    a. Construct **90%** confidence intervals for each of the 50 samples. These confidence intervals will appear in the Session Window. **Note: For this example, do not construct Boxplots or Histograms. In the 1-sample Z Window, click on Graphs and make sure that the two graphs are not selected.** When you have completed all the examples in this assignment, print the Session Window and then use the Session Window output to answer the questions below. So, do not answer the questions below until you have the printout of your Session Window. Now proceed to problem #2.

    b. Look at the 50 confidence intervals. How many of your intervals failed to correctly estimate μ? Note: Remember that, in this example, we know that the population mean, μ, is 69. _____ (Highlight these intervals on your printout.)

    c. How many of your intervals actually did contain μ? _____

    d. What percentage of your intervals contained μ? _____

    e. Based on the confidence level used in this example, what percentage of the intervals did you expect to contain μ? _____

    f. How does your actual percentage compare with the percentage you expected based on your confidence coefficient?

g. For the first five 95% confidence intervals in Fig. 8-1 (earlier in the chapter) calculate the width of confidence intervals by subtracting the lower limit from the upper limit and rounding your answer to the nearest hundredth. What did you discover?

h. For the first five 90% confidence intervals that you created in your Session Window calculate the width of the intervals and round your answer to the nearest hundredth. What did you discover?

i. How does the width of the 95% confidence intervals compare to the width of the 90% confidence intervals?

2. Do an analysis of the confidence interval process for the situation where σ is unknown. Open the worksheet CONFINT1.MTW. This file contains 50 random samples of size n=25 from a normal population with μ=69.

   a. Construct 90% confidence intervals for each of the 50 samples, C1-C50. Since σ is unknown, you will use the **1-Sample-t** to create the confidence intervals.

      Click on: STAT → BASIC STATISTICS → 1-SAMPLE-t

      Fill in the appropriate information in the input windows. **Note: For this example, do not construct Boxplots or Histograms. Click on Graphs and make sure that the two graphs are not selected.**

   b. Answer the following questions after you print your Session Window. Proceed to problem #3.

   c. Look at the 50 confidence intervals. How many of your intervals failed to correctly estimate μ? _____ (Highlight these intervals on your printout.)

   d. How many of your intervals actually did contain μ? _____

e. What percentage of your intervals contained μ? _____

f. Based on the confidence level used in this example, what percentage of the intervals did you expect to contain μ? _____

g. How does your actual percentage compare with the percentage you expected based on your confidence coefficient?

h. For the first five 90% confidence intervals that you created in your Session Window calculate the width of the intervals and round your answer to the nearest hundredth. What did you discover?

i. Compare the 90% t-intervals to the 90% Z-intervals calculated in problem 1a.

j. Suppose you created 99% t-intervals instead of 90% t-intervals. What differences would you expect?

3. For this example, you will enter the data directly into the Data Window. Start by clearing the current worksheet.

Here is a random sample of resting heart rates for 20 male athletes between the ages of 18 and 25:

58 67 63 65 59 57 51 64 59 54 65 56 59 58 62 64 55 59 61 55

You are interested in constructing a confidence interval for μ, the average heart rate of all male athletes in this age group.

Since this is a small dataset it is critical that the assumption of Normality is satisfied. So begin with a graph that will look for normality (or lack of normality).

    a. Construct a 99% confidence interval for μ, the average heart rate of all male athletes in this age group. Include a Histogram and Boxplot of the data.

    b. What do the graphs (probability plot, Histogram and Boxplot) tell you about the dataset?

    c. Using the confidence interval, make a statement about μ, the average resting heart rate of male athletes.

Note: Be sure to print your graphs directly from MINITAB or copy them to a Word document and print the Word document once you have completed the assignment.

4. Suppose you are interested in estimating the average salary for Biostatisticians in Connecticut. You obtain a random sample of 25 biostatisticians hired during the last five years. The sample data appeared to be approximately normally distributed with no outliers. The average salary for the sample is $80,080 and the standard deviation is $18,850. Construct a 95% confidence interval for μ the true average salary for newly hired biostatisticians in Connecticut.

Note: In this example, you have the *summarized data*, rather than the *raw data*.

Click on: STAT $\rightarrow$ BASIC STATISTICS $\rightarrow$ 1-SAMPLE-t

On the input screen, use the drop down menu to select **Summarized Data** and enter the sample size, the sample mean and the sample standard deviation.

Using the confidence interval, make a statement about μ, the average starting salary of Biostatisticians in CT.

Note: Be sure to print your Session Window now.

Chapter 9

Hypothesis Testing
(One Sample Problem)

A TEST OF HYPOTHESIS is a statistical technique for making decisions about a population parameter. Hypothesis testing is used in scientific research and in business and financial decision-making. As the name suggests, a test of hypothesis begins with a new theory, or hypothesis, that differs from the current theory. The researcher must gather evidence to support the new idea. The new theory is called the **alternative hypothesis** (H_A) and the current theory is called the **null hypothesis** (H_0). In a test of hypothesis, it is assumed that the null hypothesis is true, until there is overwhelming evidence to the contrary. If the data provides such evidence, the researcher can conclude that the alternative hypothesis is true. Statistically, the new theory can then be accepted as true.

Any test of hypothesis starts with the identification of the null and alternative hypotheses. A sample of data is then collected, checked for errors, and analyzed to see if the data is reasonably consistent with the null hypothesis or if it contradicts the null. This is done by summarizing the information in the sample data and calculating a test statistic. The sample data contradict the null hypothesis when the test statistic differs significantly from what would be expected if the null hypothesis were true.

For example, suppose the current treatment for high blood pressure provides a mean reduction of 20 points. A pharmaceutical company is testing a new drug which they believe will be more effective in reducing blood pressure. Their research hypothesis (H_A) is that the mean blood pressure drop under the new treatment is more than 20 points. The null hypothesis (H_0) is that the mean drop in blood pressure is 20 points. The company expects that the data will contradict the null hypothesis and thus, supply evidence that their new drug more effectively lowers high blood pressure.

Since hypothesis testing, like interval estimation, uses a sample from the population, there is a possibility of making an incorrect decision and rejecting the null hypothesis when, in fact, it is true. A researcher incorporates this possibility into her hypothesis test by setting the significance level for the test. The significance level (α-level) measures the likelihood of this possibility. Typical α-levels are .10, .05, and .01. So if α = .05, the probability of incorrectly rejecting the null hypothesis is .05.

Hypothesis Testing for a Mean:

The procedure for the hypothesis test is to compare the sample mean to the population mean that is specified in the null hypothesis. We ASSUME that the null hypothesis is true, and would like to know if the sample mean is consistent with this assumption. The problem is that we need an objective way to decide if the sample data contradicts or agrees with the null hypothesis. Is the sample mean significantly different from the population mean, or is it only slightly different? We have already learned that a Z-score measures distance away from the mean in standard deviation units. Recall that a Z-score is calculated by subtracting a mean and dividing by a standard deviation. Here we will be standardizing $\bar{x}$, our sample mean. We will use it now in hypothesis testing, and call it a TEST STATISTIC.

According to the Central Limit Theorem, $\mu_{\bar{x}} = \mu$ (the population mean which is specified in the null hypothesis) and $\sigma_{\bar{x}} = \sigma / \sqrt{n}$. These are the values to use in the calculation of the Z-score. Since we are standardizing $\bar{x}$, we subtract its mean (μ) and divide by its standard deviation ($\sigma / \sqrt{n}$). This TEST STATISTIC now measures how far the sample mean, $\bar{x}$, is from the hypothesized value for μ in the null hypothesis. It is written:

$$Z = \frac{\bar{x} - \mu}{\sigma / \sqrt{n}}$$

Since our test statistic is a Z-score, we can calculate its location on a standard normal curve. The farther the Z-score is from the center of the normal curve, the more unlikely it is, if the null hypothesis is true. To measure how unlikely the Z-score is, we calculate the tail area in the standard normal curve beyond this Z-score. This area is called the "P-value." Compare the P-value to the significance level for the test (α-level). If the P-value is less than the α-level, we will reject the null hypothesis in favor of the alternative hypothesis.

If σ, the population standard deviation is unknown, then the calculation of the TEST STATISTIC changes to a t-value:

$$t = \frac{\bar{x} - \mu}{s / \sqrt{n}}$$

If you compare the t-calculation to the Z-calculation, you will notice that the formulas are quite similar. In the t-formula, the sample standard deviation, s, is used. In the Z-formula, the population standard deviation, σ, is used. In practice, σ, the population standard deviation, is rarely known. So, the Z formula is not used very often.

Note: Some textbooks recommend the use of the Z-formula for large samples (n>30) even when σ is unknown. In these cases, s, the sample standard deviation, is a good approximation for σ and is used in place of σ in the Z-formula.

Both formulas apply to normally distributed data. In fact, that restriction can be relaxed as n (the sample size) increases. It is only when n is small that normality is critical.

Hypothesis Testing for a Population Proportion:

A test of hypothesis about a population proportion is done similarly to a test about a population mean. The null and alternative hypotheses are statements about the population proportion, instead of the population mean. Sample data is collected and analyzed to see if the sample proportion, $\hat{p}$, is very different from the population proportion, p_0, as stated in the null hypothesis. We will again use a Z-score for our test statistic, but it will look very different from the one used above. We have studied the sampling distribution of the sample proportion, $\hat{p}$, and know that $\mu_{\hat{p}} = p_0$ (the population proportion specified in the null hypothesis) and $\sigma_{\hat{p}} = \sqrt{p_0 q_0 / n}$. So these are the values we use to calculate the test statistic (Z-score). Since we are standardizing the sample proportion, we subtract its mean (p_0) and divide by its standard deviation ($\sqrt{p_0 q_0 / n}$). Thus, our test statistic is:

$$Z = (\hat{p} - p_0) / \sqrt{p_0 q_0 / n}$$

The P-value is calculated and is compared to the α-level, just as it is in the hypothesis test for a mean.

**Note: All examples below use EXAMPLE9.MTW to demonstrate how to fill in the input screens

Tests for a Mean (Z-Test):

Example 1:

In this example, we will look at a hypothesis test for μ, in the case where σ, the population standard deviation, is a known value.

Open the worksheet Example9.MTW.

The data in C1, (Example1), is a random sample of the amount of money spent last semester on books and supplies for a statistics course at a local university. Use this data to test the claim that the average cost is more than $100. That is, test $H_0: \mu = 100$ vs. $H_A: \mu > 100$ at $\alpha = .05$. Suppose that, based on data from the previous semester, we have estimated that σ, the population standard deviation, is $15.00.

The first step should always be to check the data. Since this data set is large, (n=50), the normality requirement is not critical. It is sufficient to check for extreme skewness and for outliers. You can do this as part of the hypothesis test in MINITAB.

Click on: STAT → BASIC STATISTICS → 1-SAMPLE Z

In the screen that appears (Fig. 9-1), make sure that "one or more samples, each in a column" is displayed in the first input box. In the second input box, select EXAMPLE1 for the data set you are using. Enter the standard deviation value of 15. Select "Perform hypothesis test" by checking the box to the left. Enter the value for the hypothesized mean in the Null hypothesis.

• •

Fig. 9-1

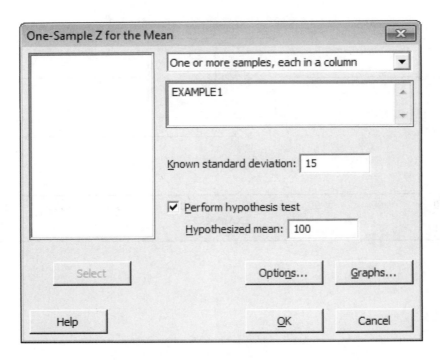

Click on: **Graphs** and select Histogram and Boxplot.

Click on: **Options** and set the **Alternative** to greater than. (Fig. 9-2)

· ·
Fig. 9-2

One-Sample Z: Options

Confidence level: 95.0

Alternative hypothesis: Mean > hypothesized mean ▼

| Help | OK | Cancel |

Click on Ok twice and the graphs and the hypothesis test will be displayed. (Fig. 9-3).

· ·
Fig. 9-3

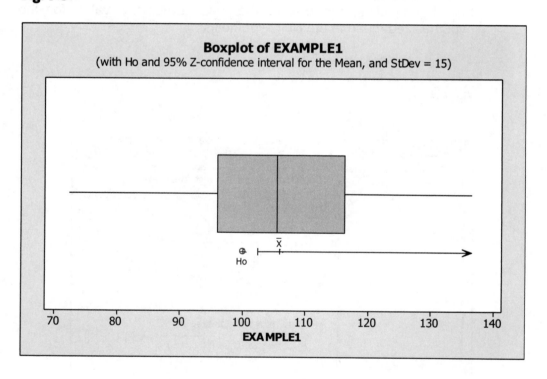

Boxplot of EXAMPLE1
(with Ho and 95% Z-confidence interval for the Mean, and StDev = 15)

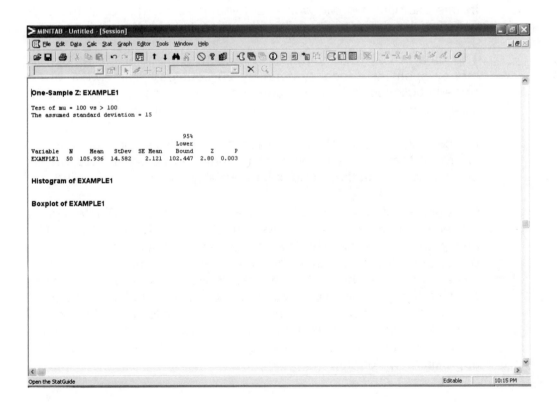

The graphs indicate that there are no outliers and that the data is not extremely skewed. The output in the Session Window shows the null and alternative hypotheses, the test statistic Z = 2.80, and the p-value P = .003. So we would reject the null hypothesis at α=.05 since the p-value is less than our α-level. Our conclusion is that the average amount spent for the statistics course is more than $100.

Note: In the output above, the 95% Lower Bound is shown rather than a two-sided confidence interval. This is because the alternative hypothesis was a one-tailed test (in this case, greater than). If you want MINITAB to produce a two-sided confidence interval, you must repeat the process above using the alternative "Not equal".

Tests for a Mean (T-Test):

Example 2:

In this example, we will look at a hypothesis test for μ, in the case where σ, the population standard deviation, is unknown.

The data in C2, (Example2), is a random sample of the amount of money spent at a local pizzeria by 20 couples. The owner of the pizzeria believes that, on average, most couples spend less than $30. Test her theory using H_0: $\mu = 30$ vs. H_A: $\mu < 30$ at $\alpha = .01$.

Notice, from the Data Window, that n = 20 for this sample of data so it is critical that the assumption of normality is satisfied. So we will begin with a graph that will look for normality (or lack of normality).

Click on: GRAPH $\rightarrow$ PROBABILITY PLOTS and select Single. On the screen that appears, select C2 as your **Graph Variable.** Click on **OK**, and a Normal Probability Plot of the data will appear. If the data points are fairly linear, then the data is approximately normal. A P-value is printed at the right of the graph. This P-value is calculated for the test of hypothesis: H_0: Data is normally distributed vs. H_A: Data is not normally distributed. If the p-value is greater than .05, we DO NOT reject the null hypothesis and we conclude that the data is normally distributed. (In this example, you will find that the sample is approximately normal.) (Fig. 9-4)

• •

Fig. 9-4

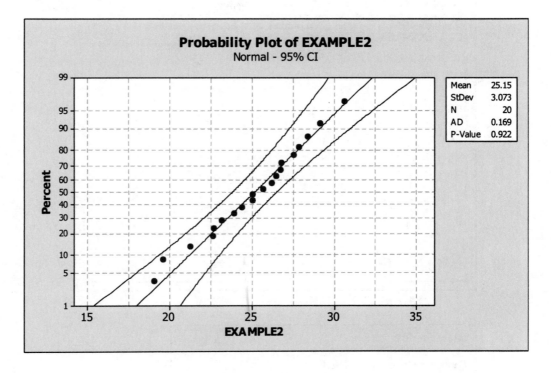

Now, you are ready to proceed with the t-test.

Click on: STAT → BASIC STATISTICS → 1-SAMPLE t

In the screen that appears (Fig. 9-5), make sure that "one or more samples, each in a column" is displayed in the first input box. In the second input box, select EXAMPLE2 for the data set you are using. Select "Perform hypothesis test" by checking the box to the left. Enter the value for the hypothesized mean in the Null hypothesis.

Click on: **Graphs** and select Histogram and Boxplot.

Click on: **Options** and select the appropriate Alternative hypothesis. (Fig. 9-5)

• •
Fig. 9-5

Click on **OK** twice and the graphs and test results will be displayed. (Fig. 9-6)

● ●

Fig. 9-6

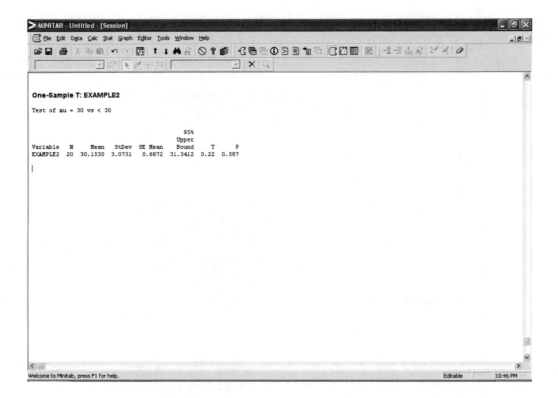

The graphs show the shape of the dataset: slightly skewed with no outliers. In the Session Window, notice that the p-value is P = .587. Since .587 is larger than our α = .01, we do NOT reject the null hypothesis. Thus, the owner's theory that couples spend, on average, less than $30 is not supported.

Tests for a Proportion:

Hypothesis testing for a proportion is very simple. MINITAB can analyze raw data or summarized data. Raw data is usually in the form of YES or NO, representing the individual responses to a question with 2 possible answers. Summarized data *summarizes* the raw data and records the proportion of each answer in the sample.

Example 3:

For a practice example using raw data, we will use Example3 (C3) to do a hypothesis test. C3 contains data on a sample of 100 graduating seniors at a university who were asked: "Have you been offered a job in your field of study?" An employment counselor at the university believes that fewer than 60% of all graduating seniors end up with jobs in their fields of study. Test his belief using a hypothesis test for a proportion: H_0: p = .60 vs. H_A: p < .60 at α = .05.

Click on: STAT → BASIC STATISTICS → 1 PROPORTION

On the input screen that appears (Fig. 9-7), make sure that "one or more samples, each in a column" is selected for the first input box. In the second box, enter Example 3. Select Perform hypothesis test and enter the value from the Null hypothesis, 0.6.

• •
Fig. 9-7

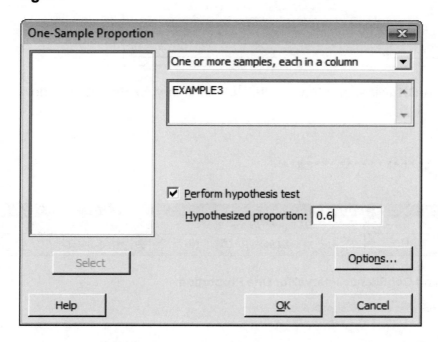

Next click on **Options** to select the alternative hypothesis. Since we are testing if the population proportion is less than .60, select that option.

In the next box, use the drop down menu to select normal approximation.

(Fig. 9-8)

• •
Fig. 9-8

Click on **OK** twice, and the results should be in your Session Window
(Fig. 9-9)

• •
Fig. 9-9

The results show that P=.033, so we would REJECT the null
hypothesis since .033 < .05, our α-level for this test. Thus we
conclude that the employment counselor's belief is supported. (Fewer
than 60% of these students are offered jobs in their field of study.)

Example 4:

To run a hypothesis test about a proportion using summarized data, suppose we take a sample of 100 graduating seniors. We wish to check the published statistic that 40% complete their education in 4 years. It is found that only 28 in our sample actually finished in 4 years. At α = .05, test if the proportion is actually lower than 40%. Using the 1 Proportion test described above, STAT → BASIC STATISTICS → 1 PROPORTION, select Summarized data from the drop down menu for the first input box. Enter the **Number of trials** (100) and the **Number of successes** (28). Select Perform hypothesis test and enter .4 for the value in the Null hypothesis. Select **Options** and fill in the appropriate information (Fig. 9-10).

● ●

Fig. 9-10

The results show that P=.007, so we would REJECT the null hypothesis since .007 < .05, our α-level for this test. Thus we reject the null hypothesis and conclude that fewer than 40% of graduating seniors completed their education in 4 years.

Assignment

• •

Please answer all questions in the space provided. When you have completed this assignment, tear the pages along the perforation. Include with this assignment all computer work that is required to answer the questions. Each graph must be labeled with a title, axis labels, and a footnote with your name and section number. If the assignment requires you to print the Session Window, click in the Session Window and type your name and section number so you can identify your printout.

1. A local university boasts that its School of Engineering attracts the top students from around the country. As proof of this claim, they say that the average Math SAT score for their students is higher than the average Math SAT score of 610 at most other Engineering schools. A random sample of n = 28 Engineering students is taken, and their Math SAT scores are recorded in MATHSAT1.MTW.

   a. What are the appropriate null and alternative hypotheses?

   b. Do a probability plot to look for normality. Report your findings here.

   c. What is the appropriate test of hypothesis to perform, a Z-test or a T-test? Why?

   d. Perform the test of hypothesis and include a Boxplot and a Histogram.

      What is the value of the test statistic? _-1.14_

      What is the P-value of the test? _.868_

      What is your decision using α = .01? _Fail to Reject Ho._

Are there any outliers? ___NO___

Is the data fairly symmetric? ___yes, not Pofet___

Can this School brag that their students really are top-notch? Why or why not? No we failed to Reject It not

f. Estimate the average Math SAT score of this school's engineering students using a 95% confidence interval. Note: To construct the confidence interval, repeat the steps that you just used to create the hypothesis test and then, under Options, set the alternative hypothesis to **mean ≠ hypothesized mean**. Interpret the confidence interval.

2. Calcium is the most abundant and one of the most important minerals in the body. It works with phosphorus to build and maintain bones and teeth. According to the Food and Nutrition Board of the National Academy of Sciences, the recommended daily allowance (RDA) of calcium for adults is 800 milligrams. The data, saved as CALCIUM1.MTW, is the daily calcium intake (in mg.) for a sample of people with poverty level incomes. The researchers believe that the mean daily calcium intake for poverty level income people is below the recommended 800 mg. (poor people don't get enough milk, etc.). Assume that, from previous studies, σ = 60 mgs.

a. What is the appropriate null and alternative hypotheses?

b. What is the appropriate test of hypothesis, a Z-test or a t-test? Why?

c. Do a boxplot and a histogram as part of the hypothesis test. Are there any outliers? Is the data symmetric?

d. What is the value of the test statistic? _-4.26_

What is the P-value of the test? _0.000_

What is your decision, for α = .05? _we Reject Ho_

What is your conclusion about the calcium level of poor people?

There ~~are~~ is sufficient evidence to suggest that Poor People Get Significantly less than the RDA of Calcium Per day

3. The TV shows "Pretty Little Liars" and "Breaking Bad" are listed among the top 20 TV series during the years 2012-2013. A recent survey claimed that 45% of college students named *"Pretty Little Liars"* as their favorite of the two shows. Fans of *"Breaking Bad"* believed that percentage was inflated (that is, these fans believe that the proportion of college students who would say "*Pretty Little Liars"* was their favorite show is actually less that 45%). They decided to take a survey of 100 college students. Each student was asked the question: "Did you prefer *'Pretty Little Liars'* over *"Breaking Bad"* during the years 2012-2013?" Each person could answer either Yes or No. The data is found in TV1.MTW.

a. State the appropriate null and alternative hypotheses.

b. Perform the test of hypothesis.
What is the test statistic? _-1.81_

At α = .05, what is your decision? _~~We fail to~~ Reject Ho_

Why? _~~Reject Ho~~ Because cie P value is lower than .45._

Write a short statement summarizing your results.

4. The national percentage of automobile accident fatalities which are alcohol related is 41%. In a random sample of 92 automobile accident fatalities in the state of Connecticut, 45 were alcohol related. Is this sufficient evidence to say that Connecticut has a higher percentage of alcohol related automobile fatalities?

   a. What are the appropriate null and alternative hypotheses?

   b. Perform the test of hypothesis.

      What is the test statistic? _____

      What is the P-value of the test? _____

      At α = .05, what is your decision? Why?

      Write a short statement summarizing your results.

Note: Be sure to include your graphs and your Session Window.

Chapter 10

Comparing Two Populations

I
n this chapter, we will be making comparisons between two populations. Specifically, we will be looking at differences between population means. The first step in our analysis is to determine the appropriate test procedure: "the 2-sample test" or the "matched pairs test." For the 2-sample test, the sampling is done by selecting a random sample from each of distinct two populations. For example, population 1 might be the Math Achievement scores for all students in the School of Business, and population 2, the Math Achievement scores for all students in the School of Education. Since these are two different schools, samples from these populations will be **independent**. For the matched pairs test, there will be some sort of relationship or "pairing" between observations from each sample. For example, population 1 could consist of scores on a Math Achievement test for all incoming freshmen and population 2 could consist of scores on the Achievement Test for these same students after they had taken one math course. Since both sets of scores are from the same students, the two populations are **dependent** and the observations in the samples are "paired."

Note: All examples below use **EXAMPLE10.MTW to demonstrate how to fill in the input screens.

Paired Difference Test:

· ·

When the data consists of two dependent samples (matched pairs), we are interested in the *differences* between the pairs of data points. In EXAMPLE10.MTW, C1 and C2 contain scores on Exam1 and Exam2 for a sample of 15 students who participated in a special tutorial session after taking Exam1. We are interested in seeing if their scores are higher on Exam 2 after taking the tutorial session.

To analyze this paired data in C1 and C2 of the file EXAMPLE10.MTW, we will use the "paired-t test." This test can be used for this small dataset (n=15) provided the data is approximately normal and does not contain any outliers.

Click on: STAT → BASIC STATISTICS → PAIRED t

This screen allows us to enter the actual data or the sample statistics Since we have the actual data in Columns 1 and 2, make sure that "Each sample is in a column" is displayed in the first entry box. (Fig. 10-1). Then fill in the following:

Sample 1: C1
Sample 2: C2

•••••••••••••••••••••

Fig. 10-1

To check that the data is approximately normal and contains no outliers, click on **Graphs** and select **Histogram of differences** and **Boxplot of differences**.

The next step is to choose the appropriate alternative hypothesis. In the paired t-test, the null hypothesis is: $H_0: \mu_d = 0$. This simply states that the average difference between Exam1 and Exam2 scores is 0. In this example, we are testing to see if there is an improvement in test scores after the tutorial session. If there is an improvement, then Exam 2 scores should be higher than Exam1 scores. So, when the differences are calculated in Minitab: 'Sample1 – Sample2,' the differences should be negative. Therefore, the alternative hypothesis should be $H_A: \mu_d < 0$. Let's use a significance level of .05.

Click on **Options**. In the box for **Hypothesized mean**, enter 0.0, for the null hypothesis. For the **Alternative hypothesis**, click on the drop down menu and select **Difference < hypothesized difference.** (Fig. 10-2)

Fig. 10-2

Paired t: Options

Difference = mean of (sample 1 - sample 2)

Confidence level: 95.0

Hypothesized difference: 0.0

Alternative hypothesis: Difference < hypothesized difference

| Help | OK | Cancel |

Click on **OK** twice, and the graphs and the results of the hypothesis test will be displayed. (Fig. 10-3)

Fig. 10-3

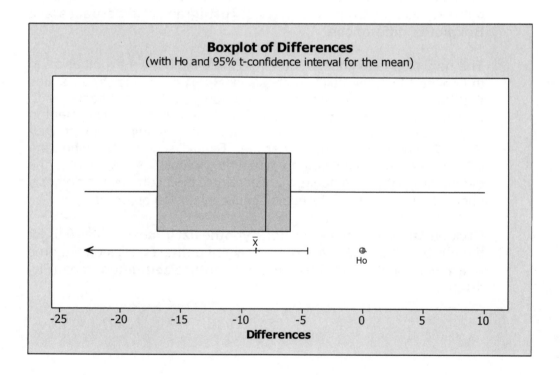

Boxplot of Differences
(with Ho and 95% t-confidence interval for the mean)

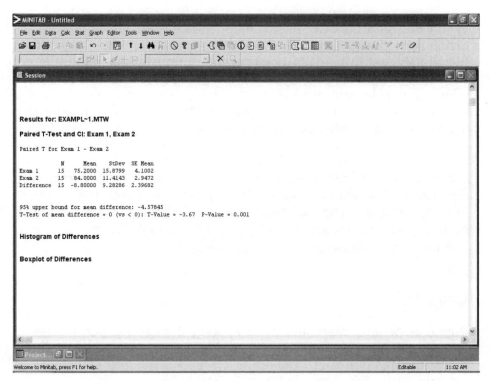

The graphs indicate that the data is approximately normal and there are no outliers. This justifies the use of the paired t-test.

Now, look at the Session Window. Notice that the P-value of the test is .001. This is significantly less than our $\alpha = .05$, and so the special tutorial session appears to have been successful in raising the students' grades on Exam 2.

Note: If, from the Histogram and Boxplot, it is not clear that the data is approximately normal, you can do a Probability plot of the data. In order to do this plot, you first must create a column of differences.

Click on: Calc → Calculator

On the screen that appears, **store Result** in C3. For **Expression**, type in   C1 – C2. Click on OK and C3 will now contain all the differences. Now create a probability plot of the data in C3 and evaluate it for normality.

Two Sample t-test:

When the data consists of two independent samples from normally distributed populations, the 2-sample t-test is the appropriate hypothesis test to use. In practice, the normality requirement is not absolutely essential. In large samples (n > 30), the test can be used even for non-normal distributions. Even in small samples (n < 30), the test can be used as long as the datasets are not extremely skewed and there are no extreme outliers.

When comparing two independent populations using a 2-sample t-test, we are interested in testing the difference between the means of the populations. The null hypothesis is that there is no difference between the two means ($\mu_1 = \mu_2$), and the alternative hypothesis is that there is a difference, ($\mu_1 \neq \mu_2$), ($\mu_1 > \mu_2$) or ($\mu_1 < \mu_2$).

Example 1:

Suppose we are interested in comparing the resting pulse rates of female marathon runners with those of female non-runners. We have a random sample of 20 runners in C5 and a random sample of 25 non-runners in C6 of the file EXAMPLE10.MTW.

Click on: GRAPH → PROBABILITY PLOTS and select Multiple. On the screen that appears, select C5 and C6 as your **Graph Variables.** Click on **OK**, and Normal Probability Plots of the data will appear. Recall that if the data points are fairly linear, then the data is approximately normal. P-values are printed at the right of the graph.

If each p-value is greater than .05, assume normality for each dataset. (In this example, you will find that both samples are approximately normal.) (Fig. 10-4)

· ·

Fig. 10-4

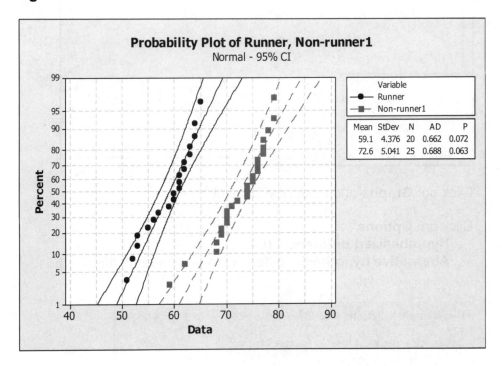

Now we are ready to proceed with the hypothesis test comparing the average pulse rates of the two groups. Specifically, we are interested in testing to see if female runners have an average pulse rate that is less than that of female non-runners. The appropriate test is H_o: μ_1 = μ_2 vs. H_a: $\mu_1 < \mu_2$. We will use a significance level of .05.

Click on: STAT → BASIC STATISTICS → 2-SAMPLE t. For the first input box, use the drop down menu and select "Each sample in its own column." Then fill in the appropriate column information: (Fig. 10-5)

Sample 1: Runner
Sample 2: Non-runner

• •
Fig. 10-5

Click on: **Graphs** and select the Boxplot.

Click on: **Options**
    Hypothesized difference: 0.0
    Alternative hypothesis: difference<hypothesized difference

Click on **OK** twice, and the Boxplots and the hypothesis test will be displayed. (Fig. 10-6)

• •

Fig. 10-6

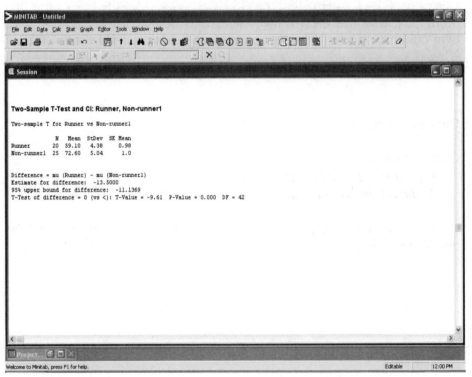

The Boxplots show one slight outlier for the Non-runners. Another
interesting feature of the graph is the line connecting the means of

the two groups. It certainly appears that there is a significant difference between the two means. In the Session Window, you should see the test results and several additional pieces of information about each sample. The mean, standard deviation, and sample size are shown for each sample. Next look at the test statistic, T = -9.61, and the p-value, P=0.0000. Since P < .05, we would reject the null hypothesis, and conclude that there is overwhelming evidence that the average pulse rate for Runners is lower than the average pulse rate for Non-runners.

Example 2:

Suppose we are interested in comparing the test scores from the first two exams in an Introductory Statistics course of 500 students. A random sample of 100 test scores is selected from Test 1, and then another independent random sample of 100 scores from Test 2 is selected. Test 1 data is found in C3 and Test 2 data is in C4 of EXAMPLE10.MTW. Specifically, we are interested in determining whether there is a difference in the 2 population means. Note: this is not a 'paired t-test' because the samples were selected independently from each of the two tests. So the appropriate test is H_o: $\mu_1 = \mu_2$ vs. H_a: $\mu_1 \neq \mu_2$. Suppose we use a significance level of .05.

Click on: STAT → BASIC STATISTICS → 2-SAMPLE t. For the first input box, use the drop down menu and select "Each sample in its own column." Then fill in the appropriate column information.

> Sample 1: Test 1
> Sample 2: Test 2

Click on: **Graphs** and select the Boxplot.

Click on: **Options**
   Hypothesized difference: 0.0
   Alternative hypothesis: difference ≠ hypothesized difference

Click on **OK** twice, and the Boxplots and the hypothesis test will be displayed. (Fig. 10-7)

● ●
Fig. 10-7

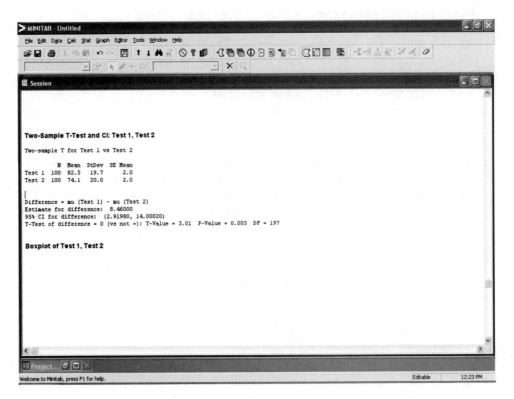

Several outliers appear in the Boxplots. Your next step should be to confirm that these are valid data points. Let's assume, for this example, all data points are valid data points. Because the samples are large, these outliers and the skewness in the datasets are not a concern.

Now look at the Session Window. The screen gives several pieces of information about each sample. The mean, standard deviation, and sample size are shown for each sample. Notice that the 95% confidence interval for $\mu_1 - \mu_2$ is (2.9, 14.0). This means that the average score on Test 1 was between 2.9 and 14 points higher than the average score on Test 2. Next look at the test statistic, T=3.01, and p-value, P=.003. Since P < .05 (our α-level), we would reject the null hypothesis ($\mu_1 = \mu_2$) and conclude that the average score on Test 1 was significantly different from the average score on Test 2.

Note: The following section is an Optional Section dealing with Non-parametric tests.

Wilcoxon Rank-Sum Test:
(also called the Mann-Whitney Test)

In the previous section, we used the 2-sample t-test to test the difference in means from two independent populations. In the small sample case (n_1 or $n_2 < 30$), a necessary condition was that the two populations were not extremely skewed and no outliers were present. If the data appears to be skewed or if there are outliers, the 2-sample t-test should not be used.

The Wilcoxon Rank-Sum test is another procedure for comparing two populations when using independent samples. This is called a **nonparametric** test and is used when the samples are small, the data is skewed and/or there are outliers. This test only requires that the two populations have approximately the same shape -- but the shape can be anything - it can even be extremely skewed. The shape of the two samples can be compared using a stemplot. Unfortunately, even with a plot of the data, it is difficult to compare shapes with very small samples. So, unless the shapes are very different (i.e. one data set is skewed to the right and the other data set is skewed to the left), the Wilcoxon Rank-Sum test can be used.

In the Wilcoxon Rank-Sum test the null and alternative hypotheses are tests of medians rather than means. The median is used because it is a better measure of the center of the data when the data is not symmetric.

This test is especially simple to do using MINITAB. However, it is called the Mann-Whitney test in MINITAB. This is because two statisticians (Mann and Whitney) did some work on the test after Wilcoxon, so their names are sometimes used for the test.

As an example, we will look at Diet Plan A and Diet Plan B and try to determine which plan is more effective. We will use a significance level of .05. Suppose we have weight loss data from 15 subjects who followed Diet Plan A for one year in C7, and 13 subjects who followed Plan B for one year in C8. Since the samples are small, we must address the question of shape and the question of outliers.   A stemplot can accomplish this for us. (Fig. 10-8)

Fig. 10-8

As you can see from the plots, both datasets are skewed to the right. So we will proceed with the non-parametric test of hypothesis.

Click on: STAT → NONPARAMETRICS → MANN-WHITNEY

On the input screen, fill in the two columns where the data is stored, and select the proper alternative hypothesis. (Fig. 10-9)

• •

Fig. I0-9

Then click on **OK**, and the results of the test should appear in the Session Window. (Fig. 10-10)

Fig. 10-10

In the MINITAB output, notice that the Wilcoxon Rank-Sum Test compares the medians of the two samples instead of the means. The population medians are called ETA1 and ETA2. Also notice in Fig. 10-10 that the above test "is significant at 0.3814". This is the P-value. The next line on the output is another P-value, 0.3809, which MINITAB calculates when there are ties in the data. These P-values will always be very close. The adjusted P-value is the correct one to use when it appears in the output. Since .3809 is greater than .05, our α-level, we would fail to reject the null hypothesis. Thus, there is no significant difference in the two diet plans.

Assignment

Please answer all questions in the space provided. When you have completed this assignment, tear the pages along the perforation. Include with this assignment all computer work that is required to answer the questions. Each graph must be labeled with a title, axis labels, and a footnote with your name and section number. If the assignment requires you to print the Session Window, click in the Session Window and type your name and section number so you can identify your printout.

1. Compare the Math SAT scores of students in the School of Engineering with students in the School of Business. Suppose you suspect that the engineering students will have a higher average SAT score, and you would like to do a test of hypothesis to check if your suspicions are confirmed. The data is stored in MATHSAT1.MTW.

   a. Are the populations independent or dependent? Explain.

   b. Do probability plots of the datasets and report your results below. Specifically, for each data is the data linear? What is the p-value? What does the p-value tell you about the normality of each dataset?

   School of Engineering:

   School of Business:

   c. What is the appropriate test to perform? Is it a paired-t test or a two sample t-test? Why?

d. What are the appropriate null and alternative hypotheses for the test?

e. Using α = .05, perform the appropriate test of hypothesis in MINITAB. What are the results of the test?

f. What conclusion can you make about the Math SAT scores of students in the engineering and business schools?

2. Students applying to law school must take the LSAT exam. Since competition for acceptance is stiff, many students take a course which is advertised to boost scores on the LSAT. The agency that teaches the course claims the course is an effective way to raise scores on the LSAT. To test this claim, a group of students are given the LSAT and their scores are recorded. They then attend the course for 5 weeks and retake the exam. Their scores are recorded again. The test scores are saved in LSAT1.MTW

   a. Are the populations independent or dependent? Explain.

   b. What is the appropriate test of hypothesis to perform? Is it the paired t-test or the 2-sample t-test? Why?

c. Using $\alpha = .05$, perform the appropriate test of hypothesis in MINITAB. Include a Histogram and a Boxplot of the data.

d. Summarize the data based on the graphs. Specifically, address skewness and outliers.

e. What are the results of the test?

f. What conclusion can you make about the effectiveness of the LSAT preparation course?

g. Use a 95% confidence interval to estimate the average difference between the pre-scores and post-scores. In order to construct the 95% Confidence interval, you must repeat the steps for the Hypothesis test that you just completed and, on the **Options** page, change the **Alternative hypothesis** to: Difference ≠ hypothesized difference. Write a statement about the average difference using the confidence interval.

3. A professor teaches two large lecture classes in Psychology. In Class 1, students are required to participate in weekly study groups. In Class 2, there are no such requirements. The professor would like to see if the average grade is higher for students who attend the study sessions. The data is stored in FINAL1.MTW.

    a. Are the populations independent or dependent? Explain.

    b. Using $\alpha = .05$, perform the appropriate test of hypothesis in MINITAB. Include a Boxplot of the data.

    c. Summarize the data based on the boxplot. Specifically, address skewness and outliers.

    d. What are the results of the test?

    e. What conclusion can you make about the effectiveness of the weekly study sessions?

4. Suppose you would like to compare the average salary of Major League baseball players on two different teams. Is there any difference between the average salary for the two teams? The data from two randomly selected teams is stored in BASEBALL1.MTW.

    a. Is it appropriate to assume normality here? Why or why not?

    b. Do a stemplot of the data so that you can compare the shape of the two samples. Describe the shapes of the two samples.

    c. What is the appropriate test of hypothesis? Why?

    Mann-Whitney test   we can't assume normality.

    d. Write the null and alternative hypotheses.

    e. Perform the test of hypothesis using $\alpha = .05$. Interpret the results using the p-value.

    f. What can you conclude about the average salaries of players on these two teams?

Chapter II

Regression Analysis

I n this chapter on Regression Analysis, we consider relationships between two variables. For example, we might collect data on the number of hours individuals spend exercising per month and the weight loss for each individual. Or, we might be interested in the number of hours 4th graders spend reading each week and their scores on a standardized reading test at the end of 4th grade. Or, we might be interested in looking at the Verbal SAT score and the Math SAT score or the Math SAT score and the Writing SAT score for incoming freshmen at a local university.

The first question we will ask is: "Are the two variables **related**?" For example, "Do students' scores on the Math SAT and Verbal SAT follow a pattern? Do students who score higher on the Math SAT test also tend to have higher scores on the Verbal SAT? Do students who score lower on the Math SAT test tend to score lower on the Verbal SAT?"

The second question, we might ask is: "Can one of the variables be used to **predict** the other variable?" Can we predict an individual's weight loss based on the hours spent exercising per month? Or, can we predict a student's score on a reading test based on the number of hours spent reading?"

**Note: All examples below use EXAMPLE11.MTW to demonstrate how to fill in the input screens.

Scatterplots:

The first step in our analysis is to graph the data using a scatterplot. In a scatterplot, one of the variables is labeled the 'x-variable' and the other one the 'y-variable.' If your goal is to simply see how the variables are related (as with the Math and Verbal SAT scores) it doesn't matter which one you label as the x-variable and which one as the y-variable. If your goal is to use one of the variables to predict the other one, then the **predictor** must be the x-variable, and the y-variable is called the **response** variable.

<u>Example 1:</u> We will look at a small sample of data from 4th grade students. The two variables are "average hours spent reading per week" and "score on a reading test at the end of 4th grade." In this example, we would like to be able to **predict** the "reading test score" based on "the average hours spent reading per week." So, the x-variable (predictor) is "average hours spent reading per week" and the y-variable (response) is "reading test score."

Open the file labeled Example11.MTW. The first two columns contain the 4th grade information.

To construct a Scatterplot, click on **Graph→Scatterplot.** On the Input screen that appears, select the **Simple scatterplot.** Click on **OK.** (Fig. 11-1)

• •

Fig. II-I

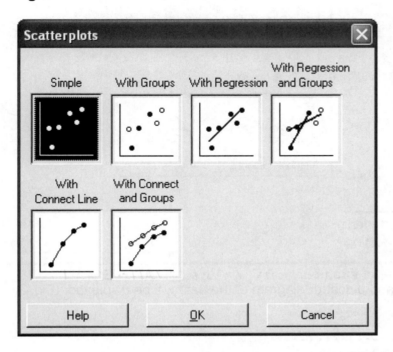

On the next input screen, enter C2 for the **Y-variables** and C1 for the **X-variables.** (Fig. 11-2)

Fig. II-2

Click on **OK** and a scatter diagram of the data will be displayed. (Fig. 11-3)

Fig. II-3

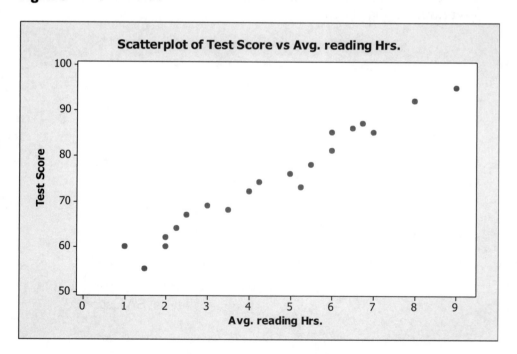

As you can see from the scatterplot, there appears to be a strong linear trend. The trend is positive because as the "average hours spent reading per week" increase, the "reading test score" also increases.

Example 2: For this example, we will look at a set of Math and Verbal SAT scores. We would like to see what type of relationship exists between the two variables. We are not interested in using one of the variables to predict the other variable so it does not matter which one is labeled as the x-variable and which one is the y-variable.

 The data is contained in C3 and C4 of the Example11.MTW file.

To construct a Scatterplot, click on **Graph→Scatterplot.** Select the **Simple scatterplot.**

On the next input screen, enter C3 for the **Y-variables** and C4 for the **X-variables.** Click on **OK** and a scatter diagram of the data will be displayed. (Fig. 11-4).

. . . .

Fig. II-4

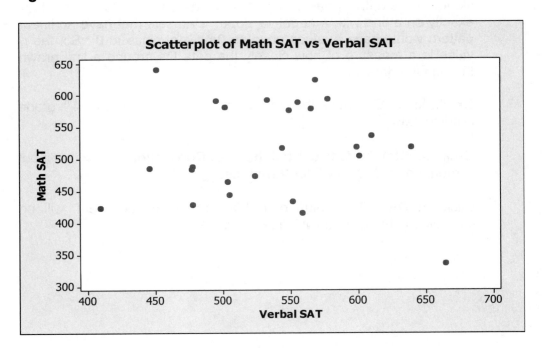

This plot looks like a scatter of points. There does not appear to be a relationship between Math SAT scores and Verbal SAT scores.

The purpose of the scatterplot is to determine what type of relationship exists between the two variables. In these two examples, you saw one relationship that appeared to follow a linear trend and another one that simply looked like a scatter. Of course, the graphs may show other types of patterns: quadratic, exponential or logarithmic, for example.

Correlation:

If the scatterplot that is created for a set of data shows a linear trend, the next step is to measure the strength of the linear relationship between the two variables. The measurement that we use is called a "correlation coefficient." There are several different formulas for correlation coefficients. The most frequently used one is the "Pearson product moment correlation coefficient." It is labeled with the variable, r, and the formula is

$$r = \frac{\sum(x - \bar{x})(y - \bar{y})}{\sqrt{(x - \bar{x})^2 (y - \bar{y})^2}}$$

Possible values for r range from -1 to +1. If the dataset has an r = +1, then the data points would all fall exactly on a line with a positive slope. If the dataset has an r = -1, then the data points would all fall exactly on a line with a negative slope. Datasets that have no linear pattern would have r-values equal to 0 or very close to 0. So, the r-value is a measure of how closely the data fits around a line drawn through the dataset.

Example 3: Calculate the correlation coefficient for the 4th grade reading data.

Click on **Stat → Basic Statistics → Correlation.** On the input screen, enter C1 and C2 for **Variables**.

Click on **OK.** The value of r, the correlation coefficient, will be displayed in the Session Window. (Fig. 11-5)

• •

Fig. II-5

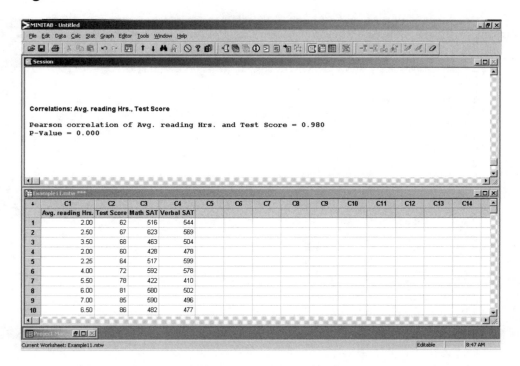

In this example, r = 0.98. This indicates a strong linear relationship between the "average hours spent reading per week" and "reading test score." Notice the P-value = 0.000. This P-value is the result of the hypothesis test: H_o:"There is **no linear correlation** between the variables" and H_a: "There **is a linear correlation** between the variables." Since the P-value is 0.000, we reject H_o in favor of H_a and conclude that there is a linear correlation between the variables. This is exactly what we expected because the scatterplot showed a very strong linear trend.

Example 4: Calculate the correlation coefficient for the Math and Verbal SAT scores. Click on **Stat → Basic Statistics → Correlation**. On the input screen, enter C3 and C4 for **Variables**. Click on **OK**. The value of r, the correlation coefficient, will be displayed in the Session Window. (Fig. 11-6)

Fig. II-6

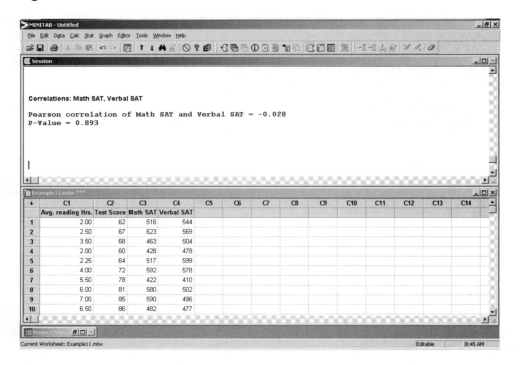

This time r = -0.28. This r-value is close to 0 which indicates that there is no significant linear trend between the variables. Also, the large P-value (0.893) means that we "fail to reject" H_o, which again confirms the lack of linear correlation between the variables. As you can see, this confirms what the scatterplot showed us for this data.

Fitted Line Plot:

Now that we have looked at a graph of the data, our next question is to see if there is a simple mathematical function that can be fit through the data. The simplest function that can be used is a "linear function" which we write as y = a + bx, where "a" is the y-intercept and "b" is the slope. A linear function is appropriate when the data appears to fall along a straight line.   Of course, the data will not follow exactly along a straight line.   So our goal is to try to find the best fitting line for the data. The actual method for finding the best fitting line, called "the Regression line," involves the use of Calculus and a method called "minimizing the squared deviations from the line."

Example 3:   Let's go back to the data in Example 1.   The two variables, stored in C1 and C2 of the worksheet are "average hours spent reading per week" and "score on a reading test at the end of 4th grade." We already saw from the scatterplot and from the correlation that the data follows a linear pattern. What we would like to do now is to find the best fitting line for the data. We can then use this linear equation to **predict** the "reading test score" based on "the average hours spent reading per week." So, the x-variable, "average hours spent reading per week," is the **Predictor** and the y-variable, "reading test score," is the **Response**.

To find the regression equation, click on **Stat → Regression → Fitted Line Plot.** Enter C2 for the **Response** variable, and C1 as the **Predictor.** Select **Linear** for the **Type of Regression Model.** (Fig. 11-7)

· ·

Fig. II-7

Click on **OK** and a graph of the scatterplot with the regression line will appear and the results will be displayed in the Session Window. (Fig. 11-8)

• • • • • • • • • • • • • • • • • • • •

Fig. II-8

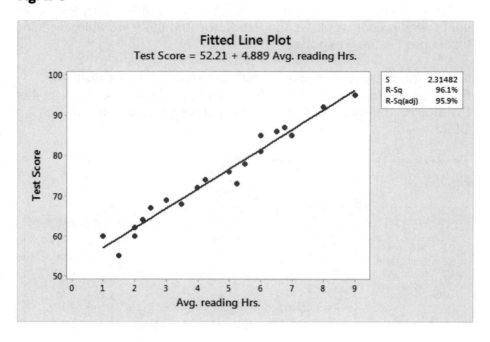

Regression Analysis: Test Score versus Avg. reading Hrs.

```
The regression equation is
Test Score = 52.21 + 4.889 Avg. reading Hrs.


S = 2.31482    R-Sq = 96.1%    R-Sq(adj) = 95.9%


Analysis of Variance

Source       DF        SS        MS       F       P
Regression    1   2400.50   2400.50  447.99   0.000
Error        18     96.45      5.36
Total        19   2496.95
```

Fitted Line: Test Score versus Avg. reading Hrs.

There is quite a lot of output produced by the fitted line plot command in MINITAB. Let's begin with the first item of the output: the regression equation.

Test Score = 52.21 + 4.889 Avg. reading Hrs.

In this equation, 52.21 is the y-intercept and 4.889 is the slope. The slope is an important statistic because it is a measure of the relationship between x and y. Specifically, the slope is the "change in y divided by the change in x." To understand the slope it is easier to think of it as a fraction. So, 4.889 can be written as 4.889 divided by 1. This tells us that for every 1 unit change in x, y changes by 4.889 units. In terms of our example, for every additional one hour of reading, the test score will increase by 4.889 points.

The equation shows us how to 'predict' a student's test score based on the average number of hours spent reading per week. For example, if a student spent an average of 8.5 hours reading per week, then we would predict his/her test score to be: 52.21 + 4.889 * 8.5 = 93.7665.

The equation also has another interpretation. It represents the **mean (or average)** test score for all 4th graders for a given average number of hours spent reading per week. So, for all students who spent 8.5 hours reading per week, the **mean** test score is 93.7665.

In the next section, the standard error, s, is displayed. This is an indication of the variation or scatter, around the line. Small "s" values indicate less scatter around the line; large "s" values indicate more scatter around the line.

The next item is the R-sq value of 96.1%. This R-sq value, which is also called the coefficient of determination, measures the amount of variation in the y-values that is explained by the x-values. The closer this value is to 100%, the better the regression model is at describing the data.

Residual Analysis:

In testing the validity of the regression model that we selected for our data, one step is to explore the set of "Residuals" that are generated by the regression model. First let's discuss what a residual is: Every data point in our data set has an x-value and a y-value. These (x,y) data values are used to generate the regression equation. Once the regression equation has been calculated, we can use the equation to predict y-values for individual x-values. These predicted y-values are written as $\hat{y}'s$. A residual is: $y - \hat{y}$. So for every (x,y) data value, we can create a prediction: $\hat{y}$ and a residual: $y - \hat{y}$. One of the underlying assumptions of the model is that the residuals should appear as a scatter about the regression line. We can check that assumption graphically using a submenu of the Fitted Line Plot command.

Click on **Stat → Regression → Fitted Line Plot.** Enter C2 for the **Response** variable, and C1 as the **Predictor.** Select **Linear** for the **Type of Regression Model**. Select the **Graph** submenu. On the screen that appears, there are different options for choosing the type of residuals that you want displayed in your graph. If **Regular** is selected the graph will use the actual residuals, $(y - \hat{y})'s$, on the graph. If standardized is selected, the graph will use standardized residuals. A standardized residual is similar to a z-value. It equals the residual divided by a standard error. For this example, we will use the standardized residuals. Select **Standardized** for the **Residuals for Plots.** Scroll down to **Residuals vs. the variables** and click in the box and select **C1**. (Fig. 11-9)

• •

Fig. II-9

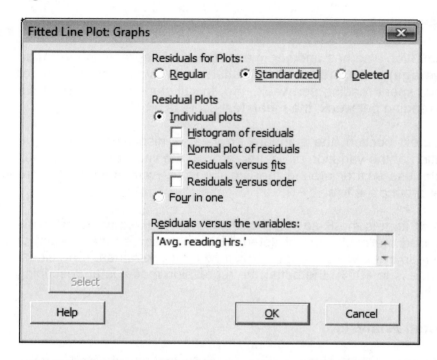

Click **Ok** to return to the **Fitted Line Plot** screen and click **Ok** again. (Fig. 11-10)

Fig. II-IO

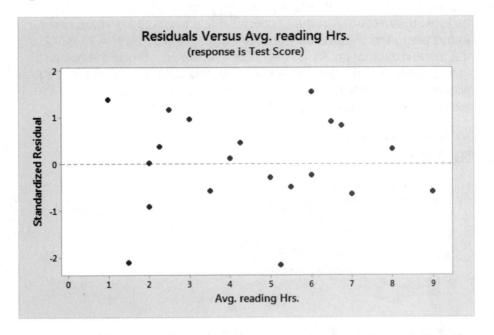

This plot of the residuals vs. the x-values shows a random scatter of points above and below a horizontal line around zero. This random scatter of points indicates that the linear model that we chose for the data is an appropriate model for the data. If the graph of the residuals vs. x-values showed a clear pattern (rather than a random scatter), this would indicate that the linear model is not appropriate for the data and we should explore other models, such as the quadratic or the cubic model.

Unusual Data Points:

It is always a good idea when analyzing any data to look at unusual data values. These are data values that differ from the majority of data points in the dataset. What can we learn from these unusual points? Do they have a significant effect on the equation of the fitted line? Would removing these unusual points change the equation significantly? These unusual points will appear on the regression plot (Fig. 11-8) as points that are "far" from the fitted line. We need a method of determining how far these points need to be from the fitted line in order to be considered "unusual." Minitab uses the following criteria: any data point with a standardized residual smaller than -2 or greater than +2 is tagged as an "unusual value."

In the residual plot displayed in Fig 11-10, look at the points that appear furthest from the horizontal line at zero. Move the cursor over each of these points and information on each specific point will be displayed. Record the information for each point that has a standardized residual less than -2 or greater than +2. For example, look at the information for Observation #17. In this example, observation #17 has an x-value of 5.25 hrs. and a standardized residual of -2.16492. Its corresponding y-value of ' 73' can be found by looking at Row 17 in the Worksheet. It's predicted y-value can be found using the regression equation: 5.21 + 4.889*5.25 = 77.87725. It's actual residual is: 73 – 77.87725 = -4.87725. Since the residual (and standardized residual) is negative, this tells us that student #17 scored significantly lower than was expected for students with average reading times of 5.25 hrs.

● ●

Fig. II-II

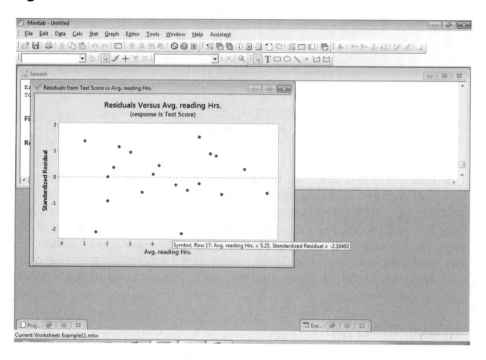

Assignment

• •

Please answer all questions in the space provided. When you have completed this assignment, tear the pages along the perforation. Include with this assignment all computer work that is required to answer the questions. Each graph must be labeled with a title, axis labels, and a footnote with your name and section number. If the assignment requires you to print the Session Window, click on the Session Window and type your name and section number so you can identify your printout.

1. Many universities use SAT scores as one of the criteria for admitting new students. But, are SAT scores good predictors of success in college? To answer this question, a researcher looked at a random sample of SAT scores for students admitted to a local university and their GPA's after completing 60 credits at the university. The data is stored in the file SatScor1.mtw.

    a. Create a scatterplot of the data.

    b. Describe the plot.

    c. Calculate and interpret the correlation coefficient, r.

    d. Create the regression line and write the equation here.

    e. What is the R-sq value? _____ What does it tell you about the regression?

f. Create a scatterplot of the standardized residuals vs. the x-values. What does the graph tell you about the validity of the model that you selected? Explain.

g. Use the residual plot to check for unusual values. If you find any, please provide the following information on each unusual value:

Obs. Number:	x-value:	y-value:	Predicted y-value:	Residual:	Standardized Residual:

h. On the graph of the data with the fitted line plot, circle the unusual values.

2. The Math Department at a local community college has designed the math curriculum with a focus on problem solving. Consequently, they believe that scores on the reading placement test given to all entering students will be a good predictor of success in Math courses. To support their claim, they took a sample of students and recorded their reading placement test scores and their final exam scores from a problem solving math course. The data is stored in the file MathFinal1.mtw.

a. Create a scatterplot of the data.

b. Describe the plot.

c. Calculate and interpret the correlation coefficient, r.

    d. Create the regression line and write the equation here.

    e. What is the R-sq value? _____ What does it tell you about the regression?

    f. Create a scatterplot of the standardized residuals vs. the x-values. What does the graph tell you about the validity of the model that you selected? Explain.

    g. Use the residual plot to check for unusual values. If you find any, please provide the following information on each unusual value:

Obs. Number:	x-value:	y-value:	Predicted y-value:	Residual:	Standardized Residual:

    h. On the graph of the data with the fitted line plot, circle the unusual values.